Volume **1** Grade **4**

Common Core State Standards
Write-in
Literacy Handbook

CCSS

Mc Graw Hill **Education**

Bothell, WA • Chicago, IL • Columbus, OH • New York, NY

Image Credit: **Cover** Wetzel and Company

The **McGraw·Hill** *Companies*

 Education

Copyright © 2013 The McGraw-Hill Companies, Inc.

Send all inquiries to:
McGraw-Hill Education
8787 Orion Place
Columbus, OH 43240

ISBN: 978-0-02-117082-1
MHID: 0-02-117082-7

Printed in the United States of America.

5 6 7 8 9 RHR 16 15 14

Contents

Grade 4

Lesson A
Use Details and Examples

When reading literature, it is important to **recall** explicit examples from text so that you can understand the most important details and events of the story. In addition to recalling specific examples from text to answer basic comprehension questions, you can also use story details to make **inferences**.

When you make inferences, you use what you've read in addition to what you already know to fill in information that is not stated in a selection. You can use inferences to better understand a text and answer questions about it. To make inferences, ask yourself what information is missing from a text. Then think about your own experiences and other texts you've read to help you answer these questions. Here is a helpful visual to show you how inferring works:

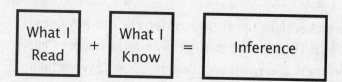

```
┌──────────┐     ┌──────────┐     ┌──────────────┐
│  What I  │  +  │  What I  │  =  │              │
│   Read   │     │   Know   │     │  Inference   │
└──────────┘     └──────────┘     └──────────────┘
```

Note the kinds of inferences that you might make while reading the text.

I will read...	I might make inferences about...
Fiction/Drama	characters' actions, events, the author's message
Poetry	the speaker's meaning, the author's message

Now look at the model for making inferences from a short story.

Use Details and Examples: Model

Read the short story below.

> The yellow bus picked Luis up at the corner. He did not know anyone on the bus. He sat next to a girl in a red sweater. "Hi," she smiled. <u>Luis knew the word and said hi back.</u> "My name's Nancy." Luis just looked at her.
>
> "Do you have Mr. Bellino this year?" Luis said nothing. "You're new, aren't you?" Luis bit his lip and stared at Nancy.
>
> When the bus stopped, Nancy led Luis up the walk. "I'll show you around." Luis had a friend, and he gave Nancy a big smile.

- One way to gauge comprehension of a story is to **recall** details to answer basic questions. You can do this by recalling explicit details and examples from the story's text to support your answer. For example, what did Luis say when Nancy said "hi" to him? Use **text evidence** to support your answer.

> The yellow bus picked Luis up at the corner. He did not know anyone on the bus. He sat next to a girl in a red sweater. "Hi," she smiled. <u>Luis knew the word and said hi back.</u> "My name's Nancy." Luis just looked at her.
>
> "Do you have Mr. Bellino this year?" Luis said nothing. "You're new, aren't you?" Luis bit his lip and stared at Nancy.
>
> When the bus stopped, Nancy led Luis up the walk. "I'll show you around." Luis had a friend, and he gave Nancy a big smile.

- The underlined text states that Luis said hi back.

- In fictional stories, how **characters** behave can often help the reader make an **inference**. Look for these types of character clues in the story. Text evidence that will help you make inferences is underlined in the passage on page 3.

> The yellow bus picked Luis up at the corner. He did not know anyone on the bus. He sat next to a girl in a red sweater. "Hi," she smiled. Luis knew the word and said hi back. "My name's Nancy." Luis just looked at her.
>
> "Do you have Mr. Bellino this year?" Luis said nothing. "You're new, aren't you?" Luis bit his lip and stared at Nancy.
>
> When the bus stopped, Nancy led Luis up the walk. "I'll show you around." Luis had a friend, and he gave Nancy a big smile.

- Once you've gathered clues from the story, you should think about your own experiences to help you make an inference from the text clues. Then you can make a connection that leads to an inference. The table below shows how you can use examples from the story and your own experience to make inferences.

What I Read	What I Know	Inference
Luis did not know anyone on the bus.	If I'm in a school bus and I don't know anyone on the bus, I probably haven't been on that bus before.	Luis is a new student.
Luis bit his lip and stared at Nancy.	When I bite my lip, it usually means I am nervous.	Luis is feeling shy and nervous because this experience is new for him.
Nancy led Luis up the walk and said, "I'll show you around."	I feel less nervous when someone offers me help.	Nancy wants to help Luis because she recognizes how nervous he is.

- The left column, **What I Read**, has some clues from the text that will help you make inferences. Once you've gathered clues from the story, you should think about your own experiences to help you make an inference from the text clues.

- The middle column, **What I Know**, shows examples of how a personal experience related to a text clue might help you make an inference.

- The right column, **Inference**, shows examples of inferences that might be made by using text clues and personal experiences.

Now turn to pages 4–5 to practice using details and examples to make inferences.

Name _____

Use Details and Examples

Practice

Read the following story. Write your answers on the lines and in the chart.

> "Are we there yet?" Jamal asked, crossing his arms across his chest.
>
> "Almost, honey," his mom replied. "Look out the window. Isn't it beautiful?"
>
> Jamal didn't answer, but he did look. Out his mom's window, all he could see was a rising, rocky cliff. Out his own window, the cliff dropped down, and Jamal could see the road winding below them. Below that were green fields. A few houses and farms were scattered about. The city was a long way away. It felt like they had been driving forever.
>
> They were driving up into the mountains to spend a week at a ranch. His mom had lived at this ranch when she was a little girl. "Some vacation," Jamal thought to himself.

1. What was the view outside of Jamal's window? Use text evidence in your answer.

_____

_____

Common Core State Standards Literacy Handbook

Name _____

2. Use this chart to help you find explicit examples and details from text to make inferences. Remember that…

What I Read	+	What I Know	=	Inference

What I Read	What I Know	Inference

Lesson B
Determine Theme

The **theme** is the message that the author wants to tell readers. Every story that you read has a theme. It may be stated or unstated. Details within the story provide clues to the theme.

Now look at the model for determining theme in a fictional story.

Determine Theme: Model

Read this short story.

Rock Climbing

One weekend I went to visit my aunt and uncle who lived in another town. My uncle was a rock-climbing coach for an afterschool program in that town. He offered to take me rock climbing with the other kids in his group. I had never been rock climbing before. I was a little afraid of heights, and I was really afraid of looking foolish in front of other kids. I told my fears to my uncle. He told me that he understood my fears but that I would be safe at all times. I would be connected to a safety harness if I fell. My uncle also pointed out that I shouldn't be worried about looking foolish. The other kids in this group had never rock climbed either. I felt a lot better after I heard this, and I looked forward to learning how to rock climb.

To determine the **theme**, it helps to search for important details that have a similar message. These related details give clues to the theme. A supporting detail in the story can help you determine the theme. Important details that support the theme are underlined below.

Rock Climbing

One weekend I went to visit my aunt and uncle who lived in another town. My uncle was a rock-climbing coach for an afterschool program in that town. He offered to take me rock climbing with the other kids in his group. I had never been rock climbing before. I was a little afraid of heights, and I was really afraid of looking foolish in front of other kids. I told my fears to my uncle. He told me that he understood my fears but that I would be safe at all times. I would be connected to a safety harness if I fell. My uncle also pointed out that I shouldn't be worried about looking foolish. The other kids in this group had never rock climbed either. I felt a lot better after I heard this, and I looked forward to learning how to rock climb.

Once you have gathered enough related clues from the story, a theme will begin to take shape. The underlined clues help you determine the theme of this story: Do not let your fears prevent you from trying something you've never done before.

Theme appears in many genres. Now turn to pages 8–10 to practice using details in the text to determine theme from a different selection.

Name _____

Realistic Fiction

Practice

Read the short story below. Then write your answers on the lines.

A New School

Last summer my family moved to a new town. I missed my old house and my friends. The only familiar thing was my violin. I spent most of the summer in my room, playing the violin.

My dad knew I was sad and missed my old friends. He came to meet me after my first day of school. He suggested we go back into school to meet the music teacher. Ms. Moore was friendly and happy to meet me. She encouraged me to join the school orchestra.

When I went to the first orchestra meeting, I was nervous. Meg, a girl in my class, was there. She plays the violin, too. We sat together during the meeting. The next day, Meg invited me to eat lunch with her friends. Now that I've found other musicians, I think that I might enjoy this new school.

1. Circle or underline the supporting details that help you determine the theme.

2. What is the theme of this selection?

_____

_____

Name _____

Drama

Practice

Read the play below. Then write your answers on the lines.

> **The Little Things**
>
> Setting: Kitchen
> Characters: JEFF
>   LISA
>
> *(Jeff and his sister Lisa are relaxing in their kitchen, enjoying an after-school snack. Lisa speaks animatedly about her Earth Day meeting.)*
>
> LISA: It was so motivating, Jeff. I had never grasped how many things we can do for the planet.
>
> JEFF: I don't know, Lisa. I don't think that the little things will add up to much in the long run.
>
> LISA: Oh, but they will! It can be as basic as switching off the lights when you aren't using them. Instead of riding in a car, we can ride bikes.
>
> JEFF: Yeah, I guess it can't hurt.
>
> LISA: Right! Neither can composting food scraps, like banana peels and smelly coffee grinds that we usually just throw away. You can really cut down on garbage this way.
>
> JEFF: You know, I guess if everyone did these things, we would make an immense impact. Wait a second; where are you going with your empty can?
>
> LISA: To do one more thing that can save the planet: Recycle!

1. Circle or underline the supporting details that help you determine the theme.

2. What is the theme of this selection?

_____

_____

Name _____

Poetry

Practice

Read the poem below. Then write your answers on the lines.

After Wind and Rain

The rain fell for two days straight
While the wind blew water all around.
And when it finally settled down,
A new world emerged, looking drowned.
After they came, the wind and the rain,
The hurricane over, but the damage done.
And the animals that survived the storm
Knew their problems had just begun.
After they came, the wind and the rain,
The habitats of many disappeared.
Some animals died, and some ran away,
But those that survived persevered.
After they came, the wind and the rain,
The land and the sea strived to improve.
But everything had changed so much
That many found they had to move.
A hurricane is a dangerous storm,
Damaging everything in its way.
Its wind, its rain, affect every life form,
And the roles that each one plays.

---

1. Circle or underline the supporting details that help you determine the theme.

2. What is the theme of this selection?

_____

_____

Lesson C
Summarize

Once you identify the supporting details and theme in a story, you can use them to **summarize** the story. When you summarize, you use your own words to tell the most important events or ideas in the story. Summarizing helps you understand and remember what you've read.

Now look at a model of how to summarize.

Summarize: Model

Read the story below. Then see how to use the supporting details and theme in order to write a summary.

> One weekend I went to visit my aunt and uncle who lived in another town. My uncle was a rock-climbing coach for an afterschool program in that town. He offered to take me rock climbing with the other kids in his group. I had never been rock climbing before. I was a little afraid of heights, and I was really afraid of looking foolish in front of other kids. I told my fears to my uncle. He told me that he understood my fears but that I would be safe at all times. I would be connected to a safety harness if I fell. My uncle also pointed out that I shouldn't be worried about looking foolish. The other kids in this group had never rock climbed either. I felt a lot better after I heard this, and I looked forward to learning how to rock climb.

Supporting Detail 1:

I was a little afraid of heights.

This detail describes a fear the character has.

Supporting Detail 2:

I was really afraid of looking foolish.

This detail describes another fear the character has.

Supporting Detail 3:

I told my fears to my uncle. He told me that he understood my fears but that I would be safe at all times.

This detail describes how the character might learn to overcome his fear in order try something new.

Supporting Detail 4:

My uncle also pointed out that I shouldn't be worried about looking foolish. The other kids in this group had never rock climbed either.

This detail describes another way the character might learn to overcome his fear in order to try something new.

Theme:

Don't let your fears prevent you from trying something new.

All of the supporting details provide clues that lead to this theme, or main message.

Summary:

The narrator's uncle, a rock-climbing coach, wants to take him on a climb. The narrator tells his uncle that he is afraid of heights and is worried about making a fool of himself in front of others. But his uncle helps him overcome his fear when his uncle explains that they will use safety harnesses and that the other people in the group are just as inexperiencd as he is.

This summary combines all of the important ideas in the story. The writer of the summary uses his or her own words to summarize the most important ideas in the story.

Now turn to pages 13–14 to practice summarizing.

Name _____

Summarize

Practice

1. **Read the story below.**
2. **Identify the supporting details that give clues about the theme. Then identify the theme.**
3. **Use the supporting details and theme you listed to write a summary of the story. Remember to use your own words.**
4. **Write your answers on the lines.**

Mario Mouse did not always do as he was told. His mother had told him never to leave the safety of their mouse hole, because the world outside was dangerous. But Mario was an adventurous mouse. One evening he ran out of the hole to see the world.

My, the world was big! He found himself in a huge room. It had chairs, a couch, and low tables. In one corner, he saw a big box that had bright pictures and spoke! Mario crept forward to look at the bright pictures.

Just then, a big furry animal bounded into the room, making snarling noises. Mario was terrified. He let out a squeak and scurried back to his mouse hole. He dove through it, back to safety. "Mom was so right," he thought.

---

1. Supporting Detail 1:

_____

2. Supporting Detail 2:

_____

3. Supporting Detail 3:

_____

Name _____

4. Supporting Detail 4:

_____

5. Theme:

_____

6. Summary:

_____

_____

_____

Lesson D
Describe Characters

The **characters** are the people or animals in a story. Most characters in a story display many traits, which can be seen in their thoughts and feelings. Clues to these traits can also be found in what the characters say and do, what happens as the result of their actions, and how the characters change.

Now look at the model for analyzing characters in a fictional story.

Describe Characters: Model

Read this story.

Outer Space

When she was little, Andrea lived near the Kennedy Space Center. Her mother always took her there to watch the rockets launch. Andrea felt a rush of excitement from these adventures. She was always very curious by nature.

As Andrea grew up, she realized that she wanted to do more than just watch rocket launches. More than anything, she wanted to be an astronaut, but she wasn't sure that she could be one. Though she was adventurous, she worried that her grades wouldn't be good enough. Becoming an astronaut would be no easy task and would require a lot of schooling. Andrea was very motivated though.

Her mother told her, "If you want something, the important thing is that you try your best." Andrea was determined to try her best. She ate well and exercised regularly. She studied hard in all her subjects. After college she learned to fly jet planes, which is an important step in becoming an astronaut.

Andrea's dream eventually came true through all of her hard work. She became an astronaut and took many trips into space.

The main **character** in a story is usually the character who receives the most focus in the story. When stories have more than one character, the main character is typically the character that undergoes some type of noticeable change. It is important to consider these clues when guessing the main character.

Read the passages and the questions and answers that follow to learn more about character.

Outer Space

When she was little, Andrea lived near the Kennedy Space Center. Her mother always took her there to watch the rockets launch. Andrea felt a rush of excitement from these adventures. She was always very curious by nature.

As Andrea grew up, she realized that she wanted to do more than just watch rocket launches. More than anything, she wanted to be an astronaut, but she wasn't sure that she could be one. Though she was adventurous, she worried that her grades wouldn't be good enough. Becoming an astronaut would be no easy task and would require a lot of schooling. Andrea was very motivated though.

Her mother told her, "If you want something, the important thing is that you try your best." Andrea was determined to try her best. She ate well and exercised regularly. She studied hard in all her subjects. After college she learned to fly jet planes, which is an important step in becoming an astronaut.

Andrea's dream eventually came true through all of her hard work. She became an astronaut and took many trips into space.

1. Who is the main character in this story? Andrea is the focus of this story, so she is the main character.

Most stories give clues to the main character's traits through explicit details in the text. These clues are seen in the way the character is described in the story.

Outer Space

When she was little, Andrea lived near the Kennedy Space Center. Her mother always took her there to watch the rockets launch. Andrea felt a rush of excitement from these adventures. She was always very curious by nature.

As Andrea grew up, she realized that she wanted to do more than just watch rocket launches. More than anything, she wanted to be an astronaut, but she wasn't sure that she could be one. Though she was adventurous, she worried that her grades wouldn't be good enough. Becoming an astronaut would be no easy task and would require a lot of schooling. Andrea was very motivated though.

Her mother told her, "If you want something, the important thing is that you try your best." Andrea was determined to try her best. She ate well and exercised regularly. She studied hard in all her subjects. After college she learned to fly jet planes, which is an important step in becoming an astronaut.

Andrea's dream eventually came true through all of her hard work. She became an astronaut and took many trips into space.

2. What are the main character's traits in this story? As underlined, the story mentions that Andrea is a very curious person. It also mentions that she is adventurous, motivated, and determined.

Another way to determine a character's traits is through his or her actions. These clues tell us about what kind of person the character is.

Outer Space

When she was little, Andrea lived near the Kennedy Space Center. Her mother always took her there to watch the rockets launch. Andrea felt a rush of excitement from these adventures. She was always very curious by nature.

As Andrea grew up, she realized that she wanted to do more than just watch rocket launches. More than anything, she wanted to be an astronaut, but she wasn't sure that she could be one. Though she was adventurous, she worried that her grades wouldn't be good enough. Becoming an astronaut would be no easy task and would require a lot of schooling. Andrea was very motivated though.

Her mother told her, "If you want something, the important thing is that you try your best." Andrea was determined to try her best. She ate well and exercised regularly. She studied hard in all her subjects. After college she learned to fly jet planes, which is an important step in becoming an astronaut.

Andrea's dream eventually came true through all of her hard work. She became an astronaut and took many trips into space.

---

3. How do the main character's actions help you determine her traits? As underlined, Andrea took all of the necessary steps to become an astronaut. She ate well, exercised regularly, and even learned how to fly a plane. These actions show that she was very adventurous and determined.

Many stories involve a change in one or more characters through a series of events. For example, a character might feel differently about something at the end of the story than he or she did in the beginning.

Outer Space

When she was little, Andrea lived near the Kennedy Space Center. Her mother always took her there to watch the rockets launch. Andrea felt a rush of excitement from these adventures. She was always very curious by nature.

As Andrea grew up, she realized that she wanted to do more than just watch rocket launches. More than anything, she wanted to be an astronaut, but she wasn't sure that she could be one. Though she was adventurous, she worried that her grades wouldn't be good enough. School was never her strength. Becoming an astronaut would be no easy task and would require a lot of schooling. Andrea was very motivated though.

Her mother told her, "If you want something, the important thing is that you try your best." Andrea was determined to try her best. She ate well and exercised regularly. She studied hard in all her subjects. After college she learned to fly jet planes, which is an important step in becoming an astronaut.

Andrea's dream eventually came true through all of her hard work. She became an astronaut and took many trips into space.

4. How does the main character change within the selection? As underlined, Andrea was initially worried that she wouldn't do well enough in school to become an astronaut. However, because of her determination and hard work, she eventually realized her dream and became an astronaut.

Understanding a character's traits and behavior is important to any story, regardless of the genre.

Now turn to pages 20–25 to practice analyzing characters.

Name _____

Realistic Fiction

Practice

Read the short story below. Write your answers on the lines.

Decorating Day

Nadia was in her bedroom. Although it was her birthday, she wasn't happy. Her best friend, Molly, had moved away, and this would be her first birthday without her. She didn't feel like celebrating her birthday this year because she was so lonely.

Her dad came in and told her not to come into the backyard until 3 o'clock. Nadia knew that her family was busy setting up for the party. That was fine with Nadia because she didn't have the energy to help anyway. Her sadness made her tired.

At 3 o'clock, Nadia walked into the backyard. She saw balloons, a birthday cake, and some friends. Then she noticed a huge carton. Her dad told her to open it right away. She opened the box and out jumped Molly! Nadia ended up having the best birthday celebration yet!

1. Who is the main character in this selection?

_____

_____

2. Describe the main character's traits.

_____

_____

_____

Name _____

3. How do the main character's actions help you determine his traits? Give examples from the text to support your reasons.

_____

_____

_____

_____

4. How does the main character change within the selection?

_____

_____

_____

Name _____

Drama

Practice

Read the play below. Write your answers on the lines.

The Opal Mines of Mars

Setting: In the future, on a mining camp in Mars

Characters: Cliff: A new miner

Jason: Cliff's friend, another new miner

Donna: Cliff and Jason's boss

Ray: An experienced miner

Act 1: *The New Job*

Jason: Hey, Cliff! I still can't believe we're working on Mars.

Cliff: What's the big deal? It's just like mining on Earth.

Jason: Life is so different here, and the opals are worth a lot more.

Cliff: I guess so... Ow!

Donna: You keep hitting your head because you are not taking gravity into account. Be glad you have a helmet on. There's hardly any oxygen out there!

Cliff: Don't remind me.

Jason: I think Cliff misses Earth.

Donna: You'll get used to life on Mars. It's not as bad as some places I have been.

Jason: I like it here. Plus, I need this job to make money. Then I'll probably go home.

Cliff: The sooner the better. I don't plan to stay in space very long.

Donna: I didn't plan to stay either. Sometimes things just happen. Alright, let's get to work. Jason, please pace yourself this time.

Common Core State Standards Literacy Handbook

Name _____

Jason: But Cliff and I are competing over who can collect the most opals in a day!

Donna: Okay, I give up. You'll see what I mean in a year or two.

Cliff: Ha! I really doubt I'll still be here.

Act 2: A Problem in the Mine

Donna: Cliff, I need your help. There's a problem.

Cliff: What's wrong?

Donna: There was a rock slide in the mine. Ray is stuck in a tunnel. He's not hurt, but I need you to help me find him. Follow me.

Cliff: How far down is he?

Donna: Pretty far. Let's keep going.

Cliff: We usually don't go this far. I hope Ray is okay. Is this where Ray is supposed to be?

Donna: Yes. He called from this level. He's okay, though he's a little scared. Be quiet now. Let's try to hear him.

Cliff: Is that dripping water I hear?

Donna: It may be. What's that tapping?

Cliff: I hear it too. It's coming from over there.

Donna: Good job. Ray is in the lower level, about half a click in. Now the machine can dig Ray out.

Cliff: That's it? What do we do now?

Donna: We can head back out. The machine will do the work. Ray will be fine. This happens every few weeks. You shouldn't be surprised.

Cliff: I guess danger is part of the adventure.

Donna: Ray, here is the new worker who helped me find you in the mine. This is Cliff.

Name _____

Act 3: A New Adventure

Ray: I just wanted to say thank you for your help in the mines today.

Cliff: It was no problem.

Ray: You know, Donna, we could use another hard worker on our new assignment.

Cliff: Where? Is the Opal Mining Company opening a new mine?

Ray: Yes. The Opal Mining Company is opening a new mine on Phobos.

Cliff: Phobos? They're sending you to one of Mars's moons?

Ray: We know how to set things up. We were among the first to mine on Mars.

Cliff: Will you take other miners with you?

Ray: We'll start with a small staff. We don't know what we might find on Phobos. After we find out, we may send for more miners.

Donna: It seems to be mostly rock and ice. Where there's rock, there could be something worth mining.

Cliff: Will you really be the first one to walk on Phobos?

Donna: That's right.

Cliff: That's so cool!

Ray: Do you want to come with us? I could use some workers who are not afraid of hard work. You may even find something very valuable there.

Cliff: I'm in. It sounds like a great adventure.

Donna: So you'll do it?

Cliff: Sure!

Name _____

1. Who is the main character in this selection?

_____

2. Describe the main character's traits.

_____

_____

3. How do the main character's actions help you determine his traits? Give examples from the text to support your reasons.

_____

_____

_____

_____

4. How does the main character change within the selection?

_____

_____

_____

Lesson E
Describe a Setting

A **setting** is where and when a story takes place. A setting can also affect the **mood**, or tone, of a story.

Now look at the model for describing a setting in a fictional story.

Describe a Setting: Model

Read this story.

Thirsty

The day started badly. Jeremy was camping in a rocky meadow with his scout troop. As rain trickled down the sides of his tent, Jeremy wound up his new flashlight for one minute. The flashlight now had enough energy to work for an hour. He would need it on this gray day! He moved outside toward the smoky fire his leaders had started.

"I am thirsty," Jeremy growled, wishing they could just go home.

"Well, Jeremy," said Mr. Kim, one of the leaders, "all our water is just about gone. The raccoons tipped over the water jugs last night and now they're empty."

Jeremy's mouth felt as dry as a desert, so he thought about where he could find water. They were miles from the nearest creek. Suddenly, a huge raindrop splashed on his head. "That's it!" he thought.

Jeremy's crankiness left as he worked. He folded his waterproof tent in half, propped it on some rocks, and watched as a pool of water gathered in the center. He filled his water bottle from the tent pool, and soon everyone else followed his lead.

As the group packed up its gear for the day's damp walk, Jeremy smiled. He had used Earth's resources to help his scout troop, without hurting Earth! While the leaders put out the fire, Jeremy helped clean up the scouts' campsite. They left just a fire mark as evidence of their visit. The scouts then filed quietly along a deer path, holding their flashlights. The day was good after all.

The **setting** is usually revealed at the beginning of a story. This is often done to set a particular mood for a story. For example, a story that starts out on Mars would likely create a much different feeling from a story that starts at the library. Where does this story take place?

Thirsty

The day started badly. Jeremy was camping in a rocky meadow with his scout troop. As rain trickled down the sides of his tent, Jeremy wound up his new flashlight for one minute. The flashlight now had enough energy to work for an hour. He would need it on this gray day! He moved outside toward the smoky fire his leaders had started.

"I am thirsty," Jeremy growled, wishing they could just go home.

"Well, Jeremy," said Mr. Kim, one of the leaders, "all our water is just about gone. The raccoons tipped over the water jugs last night and now they're empty."

Jeremy's mouth felt as dry as a desert, so he thought about where he could find water. They were miles from the nearest creek. Suddenly, a huge raindrop splashed on his head. "That's it!" he thought.

Jeremy's crankiness left as he worked. He folded his waterproof tent in half, propped it on some rocks, and watched as a pool of water gathered in the center. He filled his water bottle from the tent pool, and soon everyone else followed his lead.

As the group packed up its gear for the day's damp walk, Jeremy smiled. He had used Earth's resources to help his scout troop, without hurting Earth! While the leaders put out the fire, Jeremy helped clean up the scouts' campsite. They left just a fire mark as evidence of their visit. The scouts then filed quietly along a deer path, holding their flashlights. The day was good after all.

The setting of this story is at a campsite in a rocky meadow.

Details describing the setting within a story can give just as many clues about the mood of a story as the location itself can. For example, describing a place as sunny creates a different mood from describing a place as rainy. Look for descriptive details in this story that pertain to the setting.

Thirsty

The day started badly. Jeremy was camping in a <u>rocky meadow</u> with his scout troop. As <u>rain trickled down</u> the sides of his tent, Jeremy wound up his new flashlight for one minute. The flashlight now had enough energy to work for an hour. He would need it on this gray day! He moved outside toward the <u>smoky fire</u> his leaders had started.

"I am thirsty," Jeremy growled, wishing they could just go home.

"Well, Jeremy," said Mr. Kim, one of the leaders, "all our water is just about gone. The raccoons tipped over the water jugs last night and now they're empty."

Jeremy's mouth felt as dry as a desert, so he thought about where he could find water. <u>They were miles from the nearest creek.</u> Suddenly, a huge raindrop splashed on his head. "That's it!" he thought.

Jeremy's crankiness left as he worked. He folded his waterproof tent in half, propped it on some rocks, and watched as a pool of water gathered in the center. He filled his water bottle from the tent pool, and soon everyone else followed his lead.

As the group packed up its gear for the day's damp walk, Jeremy smiled. He had used Earth's resources to help his scout troop, without hurting Earth! While the leaders put out the fire, Jeremy helped clean up the scouts' campsite. They left just a fire mark as evidence of their visit. The scouts then filed quietly along a deer path, holding their flashlights. The day was good after all.

The setting is described as rocky, rainy, smoky from a fire, and miles from a creek.

After determining the location of a story and the text details describing that location, a reader should be able to explain how the author uses setting to create the story's mood. Use this information about the setting to describe the mood at the beginning of the story.

The setting in this story suggests difficult conditions, so the mood begins with an unhappy tone.

Setting is important to any story, regardless of the genre.

Now turn to pages 29–31 to practice describing setting.

Name _____

Historical Fiction

Practice

Read the short story below. Write your answers on the lines.

Steerage

Paolo stood on the deck of the steamship SS *Laconia*, which was anchored in New York Harbor. He was trying to see the island, but it was covered with morning mist. It almost seemed dangerous, lurking in the water like a sea monster. Paolo was very nervous, and the worst part was he didn't know why.

Paolo coughed. His cough was getting worse. It was the air down in steerage, he thought. Deep down in the ship was a large, open area filled with bunk beds. It was called steerage. Paolo and his parents had spent the trip from Italy in this big room. It was crowded with immigrants who couldn't afford the expensive tickets.

Paolo went up on deck to get a breath of air whenever he could. The air blowing in from the ocean was a relief.

---

1. Where does this story take place?

   _____

2. List some details from the text that describe the setting.

   _____

3. How does the setting affect the mood at the beginning of the story?

   _____

Name _____

Drama

Practice

Read the play below. Write your answers on the lines.

Saving the Library

Setting: Outside the town's library
Characters: Ramon: A local citizen
              George: Ramon's friend

Ramon: Our town's library sure doesn't look good. When I was kid, the halls of our library were constantly filled with people. Now they are constantly barren.

George: Well, it has certainly looked better.

Ramon: It used to be magnificent!

George: That's true. Today, it looks like a haunted house. The windows are barred up, the roof is missing shingles, the chimney looks ready to topple over, and the doors are crooked.

Ramon: And look at the sidewalk surrounding the library. It's cluttered with garbage!

George: The town should build a new one.

Ramon: No, they should fix this one. It would cost less and look better. The building still has beauty, if only it was well cared for.

George: Maybe we should do something about it.

Ramon: I don't have the slightest idea of what we could do.

George: I do! My brother-in-law is in the city council. Maybe we could set up a meeting with him to see if the city has any funds to help.

Ramon: That's a great idea! And we could contact some local businesses about getting involved. This could be really good for our community!

George: I agree. Let's get started right away.

Ramon: Sounds good to me!

Common Core State Standards Literacy Handbook

Name _____

1. Where does this story take place?

_____

2. List some details from the text that describe the setting.

_____

3. How does the setting affect the mood at the beginning of the story?

_____

Part 1
READING: LITERATURE
1.1 Key Ideas and Details

Standard
3

Lesson F
Retell Events

The chronological order of **events** within a story is the order in which things happen. A story usually begins by introducing a **character** (or characters) and the problem encountered. The steps taken to solve the problem are the events of a story. A story ends with the solution to the problem. The problem, events, and solution make up the **plot** of a story.

Look at this **Model** to see an example of analyzing events within a fictional story.

Retell Events: Model

Read this selection.

No Return Address

A box came in the mail for Denisha, but it had no return address. When Denisha opened the box, she found a blue jacket and matching pants. She tried on the pants and jacket. They fit perfectly, and blue was Denisha's favorite color. She wanted to thank the sender. She asked her mother and sister if they had mailed the package, but they both said no. Denisha looked again at the outside of the box, and then she smiled. "I figured it out! The stamp says that the box was mailed from Detroit. Grandma lives there. She must have sent it."

Events in a story usually revolve around a main **character** (or characters). This character is central to the **plot** of the story, so his or her actions are particularly important. Determine the main character in this story.

Common Core State Standards Literacy Handbook

No Return Address

A box came in the mail for Denisha, but it had no return address. When Denisha opened the box, she found a blue jacket and matching pants. She tried on the pants and jacket. They fit perfectly, and blue was Denisha's favorite color. She wanted to thank the sender. She asked her mother and sister if they had mailed the package, but they both said no. Denisha looked again at the outside of the box, and then she smiled. "I figured it out! The stamp says that the box was mailed from Detroit. Grandma lives there. She must have sent it."

Denisha is the main character.

Most stories involve a **problem** of some kind, which is revealed early in the story, either explicitly or through inference. What is the problem in this story?

No Return Address

A box came in the mail for Denisha, but it had no return address. When Denisha opened the box, she found a blue jacket and matching pants. She tried on the pants and jacket. They fit perfectly, and blue was Denisha's favorite color. She wanted to thank the sender. She asked her mother and sister if they had mailed the package, but they both said no. Denisha looked again at the outside of the box, and then she smiled. "I figured it out! The stamp says that the box was mailed from Detroit. Grandma lives there. She must have sent it."

Denisha wants to thank whoever sent her the package, but there is no return address.

Most plots within a story involve a series of events before a problem is solved. What is the first step taken in this story toward solving the problem?

No Return Address

A box came in the mail for Denisha, but it had no return address. When Denisha opened the box, she found a blue jacket and matching pants. She tried on the pants and jacket. They fit perfectly, and blue was Denisha's favorite color. She wanted to thank the sender. <u>She asked her mother and sister if they had mailed the package, but they both said no.</u> Denisha looked again at the outside of the box, and then she smiled. "I figured it out! The stamp says that the box was mailed from Detroit. Grandma lives there. She must have sent it."

Denisha asks her sister and her mother for help.

The end of events within a plot usually reveals a **solution** to a problem. Determine the solution to the plot in this story.

No Return Address

A box came in the mail for Denisha, but it had no return address. When Denisha opened the box, she found a blue jacket and matching pants. She tried on the pants and jacket. They fit perfectly, and blue was Denisha's favorite color. She wanted to thank the sender. She asked her mother and sister if they had mailed the package, but they both said no. <u>Denisha looked again at the outside of the box, and then she smiled. "I figured it out! The stamp says that the box was mailed from Detroit. Grandma lives there. She must have sent it."</u>

Denisha looks at the stamp to find out where the package was mailed from.

Most stories give an indication of what might possibly happen after a solution has been made. What might happen next in this story?

> ## No Return Address
>
> A box came in the mail for Denisha, but it had no return address. When Denisha opened the box, she found a blue jacket and matching pants. She tried on the pants and jacket. They fit perfectly, and blue was Denisha's favorite color. She wanted to thank the sender. She asked her mother and sister if they had mailed the package, but they both said no. Denisha looked again at the outside of the box, and then she smiled. "I figured it out! The stamp says that the box was mailed from Detroit. Grandma lives there. She must have sent it."

Possible response: Denisha calls to thank her grandmother.

The events the characters go through are an important part of any story, regardless of the genre.

Now turn to pages 36–39 to practice analyzing events.

Name _____

Realistic Fiction

Practice

Read the short story below. Then write your answers on the lines.

> ### Ice Pop Rescue
>
> Ding! Ding! Ding! Marta heard the bell of the ice-cream truck. It was the hottest week of the year, and she felt like she was going to melt. Marta wanted an orange ice pop—she could almost taste it. She counted the money in her pocket: 26 cents. Ice pops cost $1.50. She did not have enough money. Marta remembered that her brother owed her $2.00. She knocked on his bedroom door, but he wasn't home.
>
> Then Marta got an idea. She went to the kitchen and found an ice-cube tray. Carefully, she poured some orange juice into the tray. She covered the tray with plastic wrap and stuck a toothpick into each square. Then she put the tray in the freezer and waited. In a couple of hours, she checked the freezer. She had twelve orange ice pops—enough to last all week.

1. Who is the main character?

_____

2. What is the problem in this story?

_____

_____

3. What is the first thing done to solve the problem in this story?

_____

_____

Common Core State Standards Literacy Handbook

Name _____

4. How is the problem solved in this story?

_____

_____

5. What might happen next in this story?

_____

_____

Name _____

Drama

Practice

Read the play below. Then write your answers.

Lifesavers

Setting: Park

Characters: Eva
              Carlos
              Papa

Eva: What was that noise?

Papa: What noise? Maybe it was your stomach rumbling, Eva. I know how hungry you are!

Eva: It wasn't that kind of noise. It was more of a whimper, like the sound some kind of animal would make. I think it came from over by the gate. Hey, look! It's a dog!

Papa: You both stay here while I check him out. He doesn't have a collar, and he might not be friendly. Poor boy, you look like you haven't eaten for days. Where did you come from? Are you lost, or did someone abandon you?

Carlos: How could someone abandon a pet? If I had a dog, I'd never abandon it.

Papa: Maybe his owners couldn't take care of him anymore. Caring for a dog is a big responsibility, and unfortunately, some people just aren't up for it.

Eva: But how could they leave him like that? Look how thin he is. His owners should have found him a new home.

Papa: Hold on, let's not jump to conclusions. He might not have been abandoned. He might just be lost, and his owners are looking for him.

Common Core State Standards Literacy Handbook

Name _____

> Carlos: Maybe we should take a photograph of him, and I could create some flyers on the computer that we could post around town. Someone might recognize him.
>
> Papa: Yes, let's do that. We can post one on the community notice board at the library, and I'll call the newspaper to put an advertisement in the Lost and Found section. Eva, can you give him some food and water? There are some meat scraps in the kitchen. Then we should take him to the veterinary clinic to see Dr. Grace just to make sure he's OK.
>
> Eva: Come on, boy! I'll get you some good food, and while you eat, Papa and Carlos will try to find out where you live.

1. Who are the main characters?

_____

2. What is the problem in this story?

_____

3. What is the first thing done to solve the problem in this story?

_____

_____

4. How is the problem solved in this story?

_____

_____

5. What might happen next in this story?

_____

_____

Lesson A
Determine Meaning of Words and Phrases

When you come to a word or phrase you do not know in a passage, there are several strategies you can use to determine meaning.

Use a Dictionary

A dictionary can tell you an unknown word's meaning, pronunciation, and syllabication.

Read the passage below. Then look at the sample dictionary entry for the word *dangerous*.

> Khalid and George went for a hike in the woods. As they walked along the trail they saw a snake. Even small snakes can be dangerous, so when George saw it he became uncomfortable. Khalid tried to look at the snake's markings to figure out what kind of snake it was, but the snake quickly slithered away. It slid down the hill, into the bushes. With the snake out of sight, George was not anxious anymore and the boys continued the hike without a worry.

Sample Entry

> **dan ger ous** (dān´ jə rəs) *adj.* 1. able to cause harm or danger. *The highway is a dangerous place for dogs to walk along.*
>
> A phonetic spelling tells you how to say the word. Notice that *dangerous* is divided into three parts. Each part is called a **syllable**.
>
> The accent mark (´) after the first syllable shows you which syllable to stress when pronouncing the word.

For more information about using dictionaries as a resource, turn to Language Lesson 6.3 **Dictionaries and Glossaries** on Volume 2 page 268.

Think About Word Parts

Dividing words into word parts can help you determine the meaning of unknown words. Knowing the meanings of prefixes, suffixes, and word roots will help you.

- A **prefix** is the word part that comes before the root word.
- A **suffix** is the word part that comes after the root word.
- A **root word** is the word part that is the main part of a word.

Read the passage below. Then look at the word *uncomfortable* and the example of how you might use word parts to determine the meaning of the word.

> Khalid and George went for a hike in the woods. As they walked along the trail they saw a snake. Even small snakes can be dangerous, so when George saw it he became uncomfortable. Khalid tried to look at the snake's markings to figure out what kind of snake it was, but the snake quickly slithered away. It slid down the hill, into the bushes. With the snake out of sight, George was not anxious anymore and the boys continued the hike without a worry.

> **Example:** The prefixes **un-**, **non-**, and **dis-** mean "not" or "the opposite of."
> - **dis** + trust = distrust (to not trust)
> - **non** + sense = nonsense (something that doesn't make sense)
> - **un** + covered = uncovered (the opposite of covered)

Since you know the meaning of the prefix *un-* is "not" and the meaning of the root word *comfortable* is "enjoying comfort or peace," you can determine that the meaning of *uncomfortable* is "not comfortable or not peaceful."

Use Context Clues

"Context" refers to the words in the same or surrounding sentences. These other words and sentences can help you figure out the unknown word's meaning. Sometimes writers use definitions or examples to help readers understand unfamiliar words.

Read the passage below. Then look at the example of how you might use context clues to determine the meaning of the word *slithered* and the phrase *terribly anxious*.

> Khalid and George went for a hike in the woods. As they walked along the trail they saw a snake. Even small snakes can be dangerous, so when George saw it he became uncomfortable. Khalid tried to look at the snake's markings to figure out what kind of snake it was, but the snake quickly slithered away. It slid down the hill, into the bushes. With the snake out of sight, George was not terribly anxious anymore and the boys continued the hike without a worry.

Context clues can be used to determine the meaning of the word *slithered*. The words "quickly" and "away" describe the action of *slithered*. So *slithered* must be a movement. Now look at the next sentence, "It slid down the hill, into the bushes." "Slid" is a synonym for the word *slithered*. So *slithered* must mean "to have slid away."

The phrase *terribly anxious* in the last sentence can also be confusing. You know that George was uncomfortable about seeing the snake. Now that the snake is gone, how do you think George would feel? The second part of the last sentence can help you answer that question. It says "the boys continued the hike without a worry." George is no longer worried about the snake, so the phrase *terribly anxious* must mean "greatly worried" since the sentence says that George is not terribly anxious.

You have read about three strategies you can use to determine the meaning of a word or phrase. Now turn to pages 43–44 to practice using these strategies.

Name _____

Determine Meaning of Words and Phrases

Practice

Read the passage below. Use context clues, word parts, or the dictionary to help you figure out the meanings of the words in dark type. Write the strategy you used to identify the word's meaning. If you used context clues, write the context clues you used on the lines.

> We were standing around the **corral,** leaning on the fence and watching the horses. "Midnight's a good mother," I said, as the black mare's **foal** followed closely behind her. Only two days old, it was still getting used to walking on its long, **wobbly** legs.
>
> My aunt sighed. "Sometimes I wonder if they would have been better off in the canyon, living in the **wilderness** instead of around **humankind,**" she said.

1. corral definition:

_____

_____

strategy:

_____

_____

2. foal definition:

_____

_____

strategy:

_____

_____

Name _____

3. wobbly definition:

_____

_____

strategy:

_____

_____

4. wilderness definition:

_____

_____

strategy:

_____

_____

5. humankind definition:

_____

_____

strategy:

_____

_____

Lesson B
Understand Literary Allusions

A **literary allusion** is a reference within a piece of literature to another piece of literature, a movie, a work of art, or perhaps an event in history.

For example, suppose a character in a book you are reading describes mathematics as his "Achilles' heel." This is a literary allusion to Achilles, a warrior of Greek mythology who survives many battles until he is shot in the heel, the one place where he is weak. If you were familiar with Achilles' story, you would understand that the character in the book you are reading means that he does well in all school subjects except for math.

The more you read and learn, the more literary allusions you will understand!

Now look at a model of a literary allusion.

Literary Allusions: Model

Read the story below.

A Little Exaggeration

Sofia liked to exaggerate. "Just a little," as she liked to say. Since her friends had long ago learned to believe only half of what she said, Sofia was always happy to meet someone new.

"Did I tell you about my cat?" she asked Ian, the new student in her art class.

Across the table, Eddie and Tejal rolled their eyes.

"He has to wear a bio-suit," Sofia said.

"What's a bio-suit?" asked Ian.

"Well, it looks kind of like the suits astronauts wear. You know, with a breathing helmet on top. My cat has to wear it all the time because my dad is allergic to his fur."

"Sofia, your tales are taller than Paul Bunyan!" cried Eddie.

When Eddie says that Sofia's tales are taller than Paul Bunyan's, he is making a reference to another piece of literature. To find out what this piece of literature is and what the literary allusion means, read the folktale below.

Paul Bunyan and the Crooked River

Paul Bunyan was so tall that he took his baths in a lake and combed his beard with a pine tree. One day, as he and Babe, his giant blue ox, sat by a crooked river, it sprayed them with three thousand gallons of water. Paul decided to teach that river a lesson. He and Babe went to the North Pole and caught two blizzards. They went back to the crooked river and tied a blizzard on each side. When the river was frozen solid, he and Babe pulled it until it was as straight as an arrow. Paul sure taught that river a lesson!

As you have learned, Paul Bunyan is a character from an American folktale. He was exceptionally tall. When Eddie, the character in the story "A Little Exaggeration," compares his friend's made-up stories to Paul Bunyan, he means that her stories are very tall tales. And just like the exaggerated stories about Paul Bunyan, Sofia's tales cannot be real.

Now turn to pages 47–48 to practice with another literary allusion.

Name _____

Understand Literary Allusions

Practice

Read the story below. Then see if you can explain the literary allusion in it by reading the myth that follows. Write your answer on the lines.

Lifting the Library

It was moving day, and Carrie was tired but happy. Her new room had built-in shelves, and she was excited to have so much space for her prized book collection. She carted box after box up the crooked stairs until her back ached. Finally, there was just one box left. It was big and brown and taped up on all sides to keep the precious books inside from spilling out. Carrie had been avoiding it all day.

At last, she decided to confront it. She stooped down and pulled. Nothing happened. She tried again, this time bending at the knees. It still wouldn't budge. After a few more failed attempts, Carrie sighed in frustration.

"I need someone Herculean to lift this thing!" she grumbled.

"You called?" asked her brother Jon, smiling as he came in from the kitchen.

Jon wasn't just her big brother in name—he was her big brother in size and strength. And, like Carrie, he loved to read.

"This itty bitty thing?" he asked, winking at her. "No problem. Just promise to lend me a good book in return!"

Name _____

> ### Hercules and the King
>
> Hercules was stronger than any man in Greece. One day, the king challenged him to clean the royal stable in one day. The rich king kept thousands of cattle, so he knew the task was impossible. Hercules agreed to try and thought of a plan. First he tore a hole in the wall at each end of the stable. Then he grabbed a nearby river and pushed it into the hole. The water rushed through the stable and out the hole on the far wall, washing the stable clean.
>
> Using both his strength and his brain, Hercules had done what the king asked.

Carrie, the character in the story "Lifting the Library," makes a literary allusion when she says that she needs someone Herculean to lift the box of books. Based on what you read in the myth "Hercules and the King," what do you think she means?

_____

_____

_____

_____

_____

_____

Standard
5

Lesson C
Compare Genres: Poetry, Drama, and Prose

Authors write in different genres to express their ideas. By learning about and comparing the elements of different genres, readers can better understand what they are reading. For example, knowing that dramas have stage directions and dialogue helps readers learn more about the characters.

Elements of Poetry

Poetry creates word pictures, describes moments, or expresses feelings. There are many different forms of poetry. Two examples of poem forms are free verse and lyrical poems. A free verse poem does not rhyme. A lyrical poem uses imagery to express a feeling and uses rhythm, regular meter, and rhyme.

Read the poem below. Then see how each element of poetry is represented in the poem "Mary's Canary."

Mary's Canary

Mary had a pretty bird,
　　Feathers bright and yellow,
Slender legs—upon my word
　　He was a pretty fellow!

The sweetest note he always sung,
　　Which much delighted Mary.
She often, where the cage was hung,
　　Sat hearing her canary.

Verse

Verse is one line of a poem. In the poem below *Mary had a pretty bird* is one verse of the poem.

Poems are written in groups of lines called stanzas. A stanza in a poem is like a paragraph in a story. Often a new idea or image appears in each stanza.

The poem "Mary's Canary" is written in two stanzas.

Rhyme

Rhyme is created when two words have the same ending sounds. A poem may have a rhyme scheme. A rhyme scheme is the pattern of rhyming words in a poem.

In the poem "Mary's Canary," the words that rhyme are *bird* and *word*, *yellow* and *fellow*, *sung* and *hung*, and *Mary* and *canary*. The rhyme scheme is every other line in one stanza.

Meter

Meter is the number of syllables in a line and how those syllables are accented. The meter helps to create the rhythm of the poem.

The first line of the poem "Mary's Canary" has 7 syllables and every other syllable is accented, beginning with the first one.

Theme

Theme is the message or the image created by the poem that the writer wants readers to understand.

The theme of poem "Mary's Canary" is how much Mary enjoys her canary and his singing.

Elements of Drama

Drama is a story that is acted out in front of people, or an audience. A drama can be a play, a puppet show, a song, or a dance story that a person on stage performs for a group of people.

Have you ever pretended to be someone else? Have you ever acted out a story with a friend? Have you ever gone to see a show or a play? All of these are examples of drama.

Plays are written in a special form, which helps you to picture what is happening on stage. This special form is called a script. A script contains the list of characters, the lines the characters say, and the stage directions.

Common Core State Standards Literacy Handbook

Read the play below. Then see how each element of drama is represented in the play "The Heirloom."

The Heirloom

Cast of Characters: Greta
Oma

Setting: The living room of Greta's house in the afternoon

[*Greta has been sitting on the sofa, impatiently waiting for her Oma to arrive. She hasn't seen her Oma in several months. Greta can hardly contain her excitement; shortly Oma arrives at the house with a small wrapped gift in her hand.*]

GRETA: [*very excited*] Oma! What did you bring me?

OMA: [*Oma sets the gift on a coffee table.*] Before I show you, I want to tell you a story. [*Oma and Greta sit on the sofa together.*] Did you know that when my mother was a young girl, she attended art school in Germany? There she became friends with a woman named Berta Hummel, who drew lifelike pictures of the children from her village. Berta was so gifted that a man decided to make her drawings into figurines. [*Oma hands Greta the box and Greta unwraps the present.*] This girl was one of the first figures that Berta ever made.

GRETA: [*happy*] It is beautiful Oma. Thank you.

OMA: Berta gave it to my mother, who absolutely adored it. My mother gave it to me, and now I am giving it to you. This heirloom has been in our family for many years.

GRETA: [*Greta holds the figurine in her hand, admiring the object that had meant so much to her great-grandmother.*] I know just where I am going to put it in my room. This is the best gift I have ever been given.

Characters

The list of characters at the beginning of the play tells who will be appearing in the play. Some plays have a narrator. The narrator gives the audience information about what is happening in the play.

Greta and Oma are the characters in the play, "The Heirloom."

Setting

The setting is where and when the play takes place. Many plays have more than one setting.

The living room of Greta's house during the afternoon is the setting of the play, "The Heirloom." Because it is a short play, there is only one setting.

Descriptions

Descriptions are related to the setting of the play, but provide much more information about what has already happened before the play begins or how the characters are feeling before the first lines of dialogue. Descriptions can also provide detailed information about the setting.

This is the description for "The Heirloom."
[Greta has been sitting on the sofa, impatiently waiting for her Oma to arrive. She hasn't seen her Oma in several months. Greta can hardly contain her excitement; shortly Oma arrives at the house with a small wrapped gift in her hand.]

Dialogue

The dialogue is the lines of text the characters speak in the play. The characters' names appear before the lines they speak. A play's dialogue often tells what the characters are thinking and feeling.

The lines the character Greta speaks have the name GRETA at the beginning. The lines Oma speaks have OMA at the beginning. Together these lines make up the dialogue of the play.

Stage Directions

Stage directions tell the actors what to do. They tell actors where to go on the stage, how to move, and how to say their lines.

In the first line Greta speaks, the stage direction says she is very excited, so the line should be spoken with excitement in the actor's voice. The stage direction at the beginning of Oma's first line tells the actor that she should put the gift down on the table as she speaks this line.

Theme

Theme is the lesson or message of a play. To identify the play's message, look for clues in what the characters say and do, what happens as the result of their actions, and how the characters change.

The theme of the play, "The Heirloom," is to treasure items that are passed down from generation to generation. They are special parts of people's past.

Elements of Prose

Prose is the normal language (sentences and paragraphs) people use when writing or speaking. It is not poetry and does not have a meter or rhythmical pattern.

Magazine articles, encyclopedias, and essays are all written in prose. Stories are also usually written in prose.

Read the story below. Then see how each element of prose is represented in the story "Art Camp."

Art Camp

"I'm worried about art camp. I won't know anyone there," Brian said.

"Don't worry about it," his mom said. "You'll see. It'll be fine."

When Brian walked into the camp meeting room, he swallowed hard. Most of the tables were full of kids talking and laughing with each other. There was only one spot open, and it was at a table way in the back.

There were three other kids at the table—Alex, Kenya, and Mike. They all knew each other, but they were happy to talk to Brian, too. Brian no longer felt nervous. By the time he went home, he knew he had a new set of friends for the summer.

Characters

Characters are the people or animals in the story. A story often describes the interaction of characters, including their relationships and the changes they undergo.

In the story you just read, the characters are Brian, his mom, Alex, Kenya, and Mike.

Setting

Setting is when and where the story takes place.

There are two settings in the story below. The first is Brian's home and the second is art camp. The story takes place over the summer.

Plot

Plot is what happens in the story, or the sequence of events.

The plot of the story below is Brian is worried about going to art camp. When he arrives, there is only one spot left for him to sit down. He meets three other kids at the table and they all start talking. Brian goes home knowing he has new friends.

Point of View

The point of view of the story relates to the person telling the story. Sometimes the narrator is a character in the story and uses the pronoun *I* to tell the story. This type of narrator tells the story from a **first-person point of view**. Sometimes the narrator is not a character in the story and refers to the characters by name or as *he* or *she*. This type of narrator tells the story from a **third-person point of view**.

The story below is written in third-person point of view because Brian is not telling the story. The narrator refers to Brian as *he* and the kids as *they*.

Theme

Theme is the lesson or message of a story. To identify the story's message, look for clues in what the characters say and do, what happens as the result of their actions, and how the characters change.

In the story, the theme is new and scary situations can change to be very happy events.

Mood

The mood of a selection is the feeling the author creates using story details, the setting, and images.

The mood of the story below starts off worrisome because Brian is nervous about not knowing anyone at art camp. But the mood changes by the end of the story when Brian is happy to meet three new friends.

Now turn to pages 55–58 to practice comparing genres.

Name _____

Compare Genres: Poetry, Drama, and Prose

Practice

Read the poem and answer the questions. Write your answers on the lines.

The Sea Turtles of South Padre Island

Tiny turtles along the beach
Rushing toward water out of reach.

Hatched from eggs buried in the sand,
The baby turtles must leave the land.

As the tiny turtles
    make their way
Above them circle
    birds of prey.

Every year this same
    mad race,
Every year in this
    same place.

Their flippers propel
    them to the sea,
Their instinct telling
    them to flee.

Tiny turtles along the beach
Rushing toward the water within their reach.

1. Rewrite the first verse of the poem "The Sea Turtles of South Padre Island."

_____

_____

2. What is the rhyme scheme of the poem "The Sea Turtles of South Padre Island"?

_____

3. Do lines 3 and 4 of the poem have the same meter?

_____

Name _____

Read the story and answer the questions below. Write your answers on the lines.

> ### A Slick of Slime
>
> There once was a girl named Annabelle, who lived in a tiny little village at the mouth of a great big river. One day, Annabelle noticed that the usually shimmering water looked slimy and brown. She dashed home to tell Aunt Alice what she had seen.
>
> "Our poor, poor river," her aunt cried. "It's terribly upsetting that many people treat the river as their own personal trash can."
>
> "Is there anything we can do?" Annabelle wailed.
>
> Aunt Alice thought for a moment. "Well, we can teach people why our great river is so valuable. We can ask them to help clean up the river."
>
> Wasting no time, Annabelle raced to the library to find out all she could about water conservation. She made and hung posters around town. She even organized a village-wide river clean-up. Soon, the river's shimmer began to return.
>
> Aunt Alice was proud of Annabelle. Annabelle glowed because she had made a difference. The river was beautiful once again.

1. In what point of view is "A Slick of Slime" written?

_____

2. Briefly summarize the plot of the story.

_____

_____

3. How does the mood of the story change from beginning to end?

_____

_____

Name _____

Read this scene from the play, "The Surprise" and answer the questions below. Write your answers on the lines.

The Surprise

Setting: A park in a large city in the summer

Characters: Tia, a sad little girl; Pilar, Tia's best friend; Tommy, Tia's brother; Mom, Tia's mother

SCENE 1

A girl, Tia, swings at the swing set alone with her head down.

TIA: (sadly) I can't believe everyone forgot my birthday. When Mom said that we were having a picnic, I thought it was a surprise party. But when we got here, there was no cake. No presents. Not even a card.

(Pilar enters.)

PILAR: (excitedly) Come on Tia, it's time for lunch!

(Tia gets up slowly and stands next to Pilar. She looks offstage and smiles.)

TOMMY: (offstage) Surprise!

---

1. According to the list of characters, who is Pilar?

_____

2. What is the setting of the play?

_____

3. Based on the dialogue, why is Tia upset?

_____

3. What do the stage directions at the end of the scene tell you about Tia?

_____

Name _____

Now compare the three kinds of literature, poetry, drama, and prose by answering these questions.

1. How do the elements of the story "A Slick of Slime" and the play "The Surprise" differ?

_____

_____

_____

2. How do the elements of the play "The Surprise" and the poem "The Sea Turtles of South Padre Island" differ?

_____

_____

_____

Standard 6

Lesson D
Compare Points of View

The narrator is the person who tells the story. Sometimes the narrator is a character in the story and uses the pronoun *I* to tell the story. This type of narrator tells the story from a **first-person point of view**. Sometimes the narrator is not a character in the story and refers to the characters by name or as *he* or *she*. This type of narrator tells the story from a **third-person point of view**.

See this model of how to compare different points of view.

Compare Points of View: Model

Read the passage below.

> Matt jumped into the boat and shouted, "Let's go!" Uncle Josh tossed him a life jacket. "Not just yet," Uncle Josh said. "Let's check our gear first to make sure that we're ready."
>
> Matt was definitely ready. He had been waiting all winter to visit his uncle in Corpus Christi. Now that it was finally warm, they were going fishing. Matt had never been fishing in the ocean before.
>
> Uncle Josh tested the fishing poles and then chose one for Matt. Matt smiled as he took it. He could almost feel the tug of his first fish on the line.

What is the point of view in this passage? How do we know?

The point of view in this passage is third person. The narrator is not a character in the story and refers to the characters by name or as *he* or *they*.

Now read this passage.

> "Let's go!" I shouted to my uncle Josh when I got to the
> boat. He handed me a life jacket and told me that we weren't
> quite ready yet. He explained that we had to check our gear
> first. He checked the fishing poles. I couldn't wait for him to
> pick one out for me. I had been waiting all winter to come
> to Corpus Christi to go fishing. It was my first time fishing in
> the ocean.
>
> Uncle Josh handed me a fishing pole. It was heavier than I
> expected it to be. I imagined what it would be like when I got
> the first bite. I could almost feel it.

What is the point of view in this passage? How do we know?

The point of view in this passage is first person. The narrator is a character
in the story and uses *I*.

Now turn to page 61 to practice comparing different points of view.

Name _____

Compare Points of View

Practice

Read each passage and answer the questions below. Then write your answers on the lines.

> A.   I looked at the glowing red numbers beside my bed. Oh no! I had slept late again. I grabbed clothes without thinking. I stopped in the kitchen for fruit and a bottle of juice. At the last second I remembered to grab my bag. I ran down the block to the bus stop. I could see the other kids piling into the bus. I made it just as the driver was closing the doors. He smiled at me.
>   "Just in time," he said.

> B.   Enrique had a hard time waking up in the mornings. His mom warned him, "Enrique, no matter what, do not miss that bus again!" Enrique woke up and saw that he had slept late again. He jumped out of bed. He grabbed a quick breakfast and his bag. He ran for the bus. He could still see the bus. He knew that he had a chance! He got there as the driver was closing the door. The driver smiled at him.
>   "Just in time," he said.

1. What is the narrator's point of view in Passage A? How do you know?

_____

2. What is the narrator's point of view in Passage B? How do you know?

_____

3. How are Passage A and Passage B different? How are they alike?

_____

Lesson A
Make Connections

Reading a story or a play and *hearing* it read aloud are two different experiences. However, making connections between what you read and hear can help you better understand a story or a play.

For example, when you read a play, you might come across words that are in *italics* and parentheses ( ) or brackets [ ]. These words are called stage directions. They tell about how the characters should move or how their lines should be spoken. See below:

> MARY: *(looking at her watch and tapping her foot)* I wonder when the bus will get here!

From reading the stage direction *(looking at her watch and tapping her foot)* and the line "I wonder when the bus will get here!", we might guess that Mary is feeling impatient as she waits for the bus. She is looking at her watch and tapping her foot as people often do when they feel impatient. Someone reading Mary's line aloud might reflect the information in the stage directions by raising her voice in frustration.

Making connections between what we read and what we hear helps us better understand how Mary feels.

Now look at a model of making connections between lines we *read* and *hear* in a play.

Make Connections: Model

Read the lines from the play below.

ACT 1, SCENE 2: Dexter's home

(It is evening. DEXTER sits at the kitchen table, viewing a rock with a magnifying glass. A second rock sits on the table next to him. RITA enters.)

RITA: Are those new?

DEXTER: *(holds up the rock)* Mom brought them home from the mine.

RITA: She brought you *more* rocks to study? You must have half the mine in your room by now.

DEXTER: But some of these are special! Take a look. Isn't this one magnificent?

RITA: <u>*(rolls her eyes)* Oh, yes. It's magnificent. Dexter, it looks just like all the others!</u>

DEXTER: No, not really. This one has a funny mark along one side. You have to look carefully though. Can you see it? *(He tries to get RITA to look more closely, but she brushes him aside and both rocks fall to the ground.)* My rocks!

RITA: *(a little bit ashamed)* Sorry, Dexter. They're just rocks. They won't break.

Look at the underlined stage directions in the passage above. The stage directions tell us that Rita *rolls her eyes.* When people roll their eyes, they show that they think something is silly. If Rita is rolling her eyes, we can guess that she thinks Dexter's rock is silly.

Now let's look at what Rita says in the underlined passage above. Rita says that Dexter's rock is "magnificent." If she is rolling her eyes, though, we can guess that she means just the opposite. She really means that Dexter's rock is not magnificent at all. She thinks it looks just like all the others.

The person reading Rita's underlined lines will say the words in a very sarcastic voice: "Oh, yes. It's magnificent." The stage directions *(rolls her eyes)* show that Rita doesn't mean what she says. She thinks that Dexter's rocks aren't magnificent at all. Making the connection between what we read in the text and what we hear read aloud helps us determine how Rita feels.

Follow the steps below to listen to an audio version of the play. Pay attention to how the reader's voice reflects the information in the stage directions in order to show how Rita feels.

Type in your *Common Core State Standards Literacy eHandbook* address into your browser's address bar.

1. Click on Part 1 Reading: Literature in the first Table of Contents.
2. Go to 1.3 in the second Table of Contents.
3. Click on Lesson A Make Connections.
4. Click on Model.
5. Click on Listen.

Now turn to pages 65–66 to practice making connections between what you read and what you hear in another play.

Name _____

Make Connections

Practice

Reread the bold passages from the play, paying particular attention to them. Then answer the questions. Write your answers on the lines.

> **Jai:** (*pulls* Mataji *away*) Mataji, I don't want to meet him.
>   **He's so old! And Pitaji says he has peculiar ideas. Let's go home.**
>
> Mataji: Let me worry about that. You come with me.
>
> (Mataji *squeezes her way through the crowd. As she and Jai make their way to the front, they accidentally bump into a large man.*)
>
> Man: Hey! Watch it! I could push you right back, you know.
>
> Gandhi: A big man can do many things. But can you forgive?
>   The weak can never forgive. Forgiveness is the attribute of the strong.
>
> (*Suddenly* Mataji *and* Jai *find themselves standing right in front of Gandhi. At age sixty, he is a skinny man. He sits before them dressed in a simple white cotton cloth called a* dhoti *[DHO-tee]. He has kind eyes and wears round glasses.*)
>
> Mataji: Gandhiji! We are so grateful to your doctor. He took care of my son Jai today. (*She nudges her son.*)
>
> Jai: (*mumbles*) Thank you, Gandhiji.
>
> Gandhi: (*smiles*) Your son looks like a good boy. I am happy that he will improve.

Name _____

1. Reread the bold passages from the play. Based on what you learn from the stage directions and what Jai says, do you think he truly feels grateful to Gandhi? Why or why not?

_____

_____

Now listen to an audio version of the same lines by following these directions.

- Type in your *Common Core State Standards Literacy eHandbook* address into your browser's address bar.
- Click on Part 1 Reading: Literature in the first Table of Contents.
- Go to 1.3 in the second Table of Contents.
- Click on Lesson A Make Connections.
- Click on Model.
- Click on Practice and then click on Listen.

Pay attention to how the reader's voice reflects the information in the stage directions to show how Jai feels.

2. Think about how the person reading Jai's lines uses her voice to show how Jai feels about Gandhi. Does the way the person reads Jai's lines make you want to change or keep your answer to Question 1? Why or why not?

_____

_____

3. How does making connections between what you read and hear help you understand how Jai feels?

_____

_____

Lesson B
Compare Themes and Topics Across Cultures

Comparing and contrasting two different stories can help you better understand common topics, patterns of events, and themes in stories from different cultures.

The **topic** is the subject of a story. A common topic in many stories is the struggle between good and evil. The **pattern of events** is what happens in the story. One common pattern of events is the hero's quest. The main character goes on a journey to achieve a goal or solve a problem. The **theme** of a story is its central idea or message about life. Sometimes the theme is expressed as a **moral**, or lesson, such as "look before you leap."

In this lesson, you will learn how to compare and contrast the topics, patterns of events, and themes in different kinds of stories.

Compare and Contrast Myths

A **myth** is a fictional story about a culture's beliefs and traditions. The characters in myths are often gods and goddesses who have extraordinary powers or people who do amazing things.

Read the myths that follow and see how to compare their topics, patterns of events, and themes.

Thor's Hammer

Long ago, in the far North, the thunder god Thor discovered that Thrym, the giant king, had taken his hammer. "To get your hammer back, you must bring Freya to be my bride," Thrym demanded. The goddess Freya did not want to marry Thrym. The gods decided that Thor would dress as a bride and pretend to be Freya. Dressed as a bride, Thor went to Thrym's cold mountain home. The disguise fooled Thrym. He ordered that Thor's hammer be laid in the lap of the bride. At that, Thor grabbed his hammer, struck Thrym with it, and left the land of the giants.

Perseus and Medusa

"Bring me the head of the monster woman Medusa!" the king said to Perseus. The king gave this command because he was sure that it was an impossible task for the young boy. Medusa had snakes for hair, and one look at her turned people to stone. The king knew that Perseus might never return if he attempted to follow the king's command. Then the king would be free to marry Perseus's mother. But Perseus knew that his mother disliked the king and would not marry him unless she was forced to. So Perseus decided to accept the king's task. First he got a shield from the goddess Athena. Then he got a sickle from the god Hermes. Once in Medusa's lair, he used the shield as a mirror to reflect Medusa's head. He raised the sickle and brought it down. Perseus took the head to the king, who looked directly at it and turned to stone.

Now, compare the topics, patterns of events, and themes of the myths.

Topic

The subject of both of these myths is the struggle between good and evil.

In "Thor's Hammer," the struggle is between the evil Thrym and the thunder god Thor. Thrym steals Thor's hammer in order to force Freya to be his bride. Thor must use his mind as well as his strength in order to defeat Thrym.

In "Perseus and Medusa," the struggle is between the evil king and the young boy Perseus. The king gives Perseus what he believes to be an impossible task so that he can force Perseus's mother to marry him. Perseus must use his mind as well as his strength in order to complete the task and defeat the king.

Pattern of Events

The pattern of events in both myths is the hero's quest.

In "Thor's Hammer," Thor goes on a quest to get his hammer and help Freya. He follows a step-by-step process to succeed on his quest. First he dresses as Freya, next he waits until the hammer is laid in his lap, and then he strikes Thrym with the hammer.

In "Perseus and the King," Perseus goes on a quest to bring the king Medusa's head and help his mother. He also follows a step-by-step process to succeed on his quest. First he gets a shield from Athena. Then he gets a sickle from Hermes. He uses the shield to find Medusa's head and the sickle to remove it. Then he brings the head to the king, who turns to stone.

Theme

The message in both stories is that the key to successfully completing any task is to use one's mind as well as one's strength.

In "Thor's Hammer," Thor uses his mind to fool Thrym into believing that he is Freya. By doing so, he is able to get his hammer and defeat Thrym.

In "Perseus and the King," Perseus uses his mind by treating the shield as a mirror. By doing so, he does not have to look at Medusa directly. This helps him remove her head and defeat the king.

Now turn to pages 70–71 to practice comparing and contrasting myths.

Name _____

Compare and Contrast Myths

Practice

Read the two myths and answer the questions that follow.

Hercules and the King

Hercules was stronger than any man in Greece. One day, the king challenged him to clean the royal stable in one day. The rich king kept thousands of cattle, so he knew the task was impossible.

Hercules agreed to try and thought of a plan. First he tore a hole in the wall at each end of the stable. Then he grabbed a nearby river and pushed it into the hole. The water rushed through the stable and out the hole on the far wall, washing the stable clean. Using both his strength and his brain, Hercules had done what the king asked.

Isis and Osiris

A wise king and queen named Osiris and Isis once ruled the land of Egypt. All was well until Set, Osiris's jealous brother, plotted to take over the throne. First he had his craftsmen build a beautiful golden trunk that would exactly match his brother's measurements. Then he brought the trunk to Osiris's court and offered it as a gift to anyone who could fit inside. After convincing Osiris to try it out, Set and his followers nailed down the lid and threw the trunk into the Nile River before Osiris's guards could stop them.

Isis, Osiris's brave and loyal wife, set out to find the trunk and release him. She wandered a long time over a vast distance until at last she heard that the golden trunk had been discovered in a faraway land called Byblos. Reaching Byblos after a difficult journey, Isis learned that the trunk had washed ashore and became stuck in a bush. The bush eventually sprouted into a large tree, which the king of Byblos cut down and used as a pillar in his palace.

Name _____

Isis and Osiris

A wise king and queen named Osiris and Isis once ruled the land of Egypt. All was well until Set, Osiris's jealous brother, plotted to take over the throne. First he had his craftsmen build a beautiful golden trunk that would exactly match his brother's measurements. Then he brought the trunk to Osiris's court and offered it as a gift to anyone who could fit inside. After convincing Osiris to try it out, Set and his followers nailed down the lid and threw the trunk into the Nile River before Osiris's guards could stop them.

Isis, Osiris's brave and loyal wife, set out to find the trunk and release him. She wandered a long time over a vast distance until at last she heard that the golden trunk had been discovered in a faraway land called Byblos. Reaching Byblos after a difficult journey, Isis learned that the trunk had washed ashore and became stuck in a bush. The bush eventually sprouted into a large tree, which the king of Byblos cut down and used as a pillar in his palace.

---

1. How are topics of the myths similar and/or different?

_____

_____

_____

2. How are the patterns of events in the myths similar and/or different?

_____

_____

_____

3. How are the themes of the myths similar and/or different?

_____

_____

Compare and Contrast Fables

Another kind of story is a **fable**. A fable is a short story that usually has animal characters with human traits and feelings. The theme of a fable is often expressed as a moral, or lesson.

Read the fables below and see how to compare and contrast their topics, patterns of events, and themes.

A Chinese Fable

A young man wanted to get a fox skin to please his new bride. He searched until he caught a fox by the tail. With great happiness at his success, he said to the fox, "My bride wants a fox coat. Can you give me your skin?" The fox recognized trouble and thought quickly about how to save himself. "I will be happy to do that, but I can't help you when you hold my tail so tightly. Please let go, and I'll immediately give you my skin." The man let go, and the fox ran away laughing.

A Greek Fable

A wolf caught a young goat returning from the pasture. The goat knew that he couldn't escape, but he thought that he could fool the wolf. The goat said, "I know that you'll eat me, my friend, but I'd like just one favor from you. Would you play a tune so that I can dance once last time?" The wolf took out his pipes and played. Some dogs heard the music and became curious. They saw the wolf and began to chase him. The wolf knew that he'd been fooled. He said to the goat, "I got what I deserved; I'm a hunter, not a musician."

Now, compare the topics, patterns of events, and themes of the fables.

Topic

The subject of both of these fables is the conflict between the hunter and its prey.

In the Chinese fable, the conflict is between a young man and a fox. The young man wants to catch the fox for a foolish reason: to make a fancy coat for his bride.

In the Greek fable, the conflict is between a wolf and goat. The wolf wants to catch the goat for legitimate reason: to get food.

Pattern of Events

The pattern of events is similar in both fables. First a hunter catches his prey. Then the clever prey tricks the foolish hunter. At the end, the prey gets away.

In the Chinese fable, the fox asks the young man to let him go for a minute because his tail is being held too tightly. When the man lets him go, the fox runs away.

In the Greek fable, the goat asks the wolf to play him a tune so that he can dance one more time. Hearing the music, dogs come and chase the wolf and the goat gets away.

Theme

The moral, or lesson, in both fables is that being smart can sometimes triumph over being strong.

In the Chinese fable, the fox realizes that he can't escape, so he uses his mind to outsmart the young man.

In the Greek fable, the goat realizes that he can't escape, so he uses his mind to outsmart the wolf.

Now turn to pages 74–75 to practice comparing and contrasting fables.

Name _____

Compare and Contrast Fables

Practice

Read the two fables and answer the questions that follow.

The Ant and the Butterfly

An ant passed a butterfly in a cocoon, about to finish its change. The butterfly moved its tail, catching the ant's attention. The ant saw the butterfly all wrapped up in its cocoon. The ant boasted, "Look at you, stuck there. You are not able to move while I can run and play." The butterfly did not reply. A few days later, the ant passed the spot again. The butterfly was gone. Only the cocoon remained. The ant wondered what happened to the creature inside when above him, a beautiful butterfly spread its wings.

"Boast now that you can run and play," said the butterfly. He flapped his wings and flew high in the sky.

The Hare and the Tortoise

One day a hare passed a tortoise plodding along on her way. The hare made fun of the tortoise's short legs and slow pace.

"I am twice as fast as you," the hare boasted. "The tortoise said, "I may have short legs. I may not be as fast as you. Yet, I bet I can beat you in a race."

The hare laughed at such a silly idea. He quickly agreed to the race. During the race, the hare knew he would win. He was sleepy, so he decided to rest on the side of the road. The hare fell asleep. When he woke up, he hurried to finish the race. The tortoise had already crossed the finish line. "Slow and steady wins the race," he said.

Name _____

1. How are topics of the fables similar and/or different?

_____

_____

_____

2. How are the patterns of events in the fables similar and/or different?

_____

_____

_____

3. How are the themes of the fables similar and/or different?

_____

_____

_____

Compare and Contrast Folktales

A **folktale** is a traditional story that has been handed down through the generations. Many folktales have a trickster as the main character. The trickster character tricks other characters to get what he or she wants. Sometimes, though, the trickster gets tricked. The theme of a folktale is often expressed as a moral, or lesson.

Read the folktales and see how to compare and contrast their topics, patterns of events, and themes.

The Story of Anansi the Spider

Anansi the spider was greedy. One day, Turtle came to visit as Anansi was about to eat his dinner.

"What a nice dinner!" said Turtle. To be polite, Anansi had to offer to share the food. Still, he did not want to.

"You can join me," said Anansi. "But first, clean your hands." Turtle's hands were dirty. He went to the river and washed. When he came back, Anansi had started to eat.

"Your hands are still dirty!" Anansi said.

Turtle looked down. On his way back, he had walked through mud. So he went and washed again. When he returned, he found that Anansi had eaten all the food.

"Tomorrow you must come to my house to share my dinner," said Turtle.

The next day, a hungry Anansi met Turtle at the river. Turtle dove into the water to his home on the river bottom. Anansi jumped into the water and tried to swim down, but he was too light. Then, Anansi put stones in his pockets and sank down to Turtle's home. Turtle had started to eat.

Turtle looked at Anansi and said, "It is not polite to eat with your coat on. You must take it off." Anansi took off his coat. Without the stones, he was light again. He floated up to the surface. From there, he watched Turtle finish his meal.

The Tale of Coyote and Hen

One day, Coyote came upon Hen. She was sitting on a tree branch. Coyote was hungry. He decided that he would eat Hen. But how could he reach her? She was much too high in the tree. Coyote thought and thought. Then he had an idea.

"Oh, Hen," he sighed. "I am so happy! I bring great news." She was interested, but she did not trust Coyote. "A treaty has been signed," said Coyote. "All the animals have signed it. It says that we are all friends now. There will be no more fighting! Please come down from the tree. I am so happy. I would like to give you a big hug."

"Ah," thought Hen. Now she knew what Coyote was up to.

"I would love to," said Hen. "But I see that someone else is coming."

"Really?" asked Coyote. "Who is it?"

"It is Dog," said Hen. Coyote began to shake. Dog scared him.

"He must have heard the news, too," said Hen. "He looks so happy! His eyes are bright and he is so fast. I think he wants to hug you."

Coyote took off running as fast as he could. Up in the tree, Hen smiled.

Now, compare the topics, patterns of events, and themes of the folktales.

Topic

The subject of both of these folktales is how tricksters sometimes get tricked.

In "The Story of Anansi the Spider," Anansi tricks Turtle, but then Turtle tricks Anansi.

In "The Tale of Coyote and Hen," Coyote tries to trick Hen, but Hen ends up tricking Coyote.

Pattern of Events

The pattern of events is similar in these folktales. First the trickster tricks (or tries to trick) another character. Then the other character plays the same trick on the trickster.

In "The Story of Anansi the Spider," Anansi prevents Turtle from sharing his dinner by tricking him into washing his hands several times. At the end of the story, Turtle prevents Anansi from sharing his dinner by tricking him into emptying his pockets so that he floats to the surface.

In "The Tale of Coyote and Hen," Coyote tries to trick Hen by telling her that all the animals have signed a treaty and are friends now. At the end of the story, Hen tricks Coyote by acting as though she believes the treaty story and telling Coyote that she sees Dog coming to give him a hug.

Theme

As a result of having their own trick played back on them, the trickster characters in both stories must learn an important lesson.

In "The Story of Anansi the Spider," Anansi must learn not to be greedy. Because Anansi tricks Turtle to avoid having to share his dinner, he in turn is tricked by Turtle and doesn't get to share Turtle's dinner.

In the "The Tale of Coyote and Hen," Coyote must learn that he can't get what he wants by being dishonest. When he tries to get Hen out of the tree by playing a trick on her, Hen in turn plays the same trick on him to get him to leave.

Now turn to pages 79–80 to practice comparing and contrasting folktales.

Name _____

Compare and Contrast Folktales

Practice

Read the two folktales and answer the questions on the following page.

Molly Whuppie

Many years ago, three girls were lost in a dark, gloomy forest. They found a giant's home. The girls pleaded with the giant to give them food and shelter for the night. The giant planned a trick to get rid of the girls. He placed straw necklaces around their necks. Then he placed gold necklaces around his own three daughters' necks. Molly Whuppie was suspicious, so she switched the necklaces. In the night, the giant grabbed the girls wearing the straw necklaces. Fooled into thinking they were his guests rather than his own daughters, he took them deep into the woods and left them there. Meanwhile, Molly Whuppie and her sisters safely escaped from the giant's house, taking extra food and a map with them.

The Catch of the Day

A greedy, competitive fisher once decided to trick people on their way to sell goods at the market. As each person arrived at the log bridge, the fisher shook it to convince the person that it was unsafe to cross with so much merchandise. Finally, the people who were tricked discovered what the fisher was up to and decided to trick him. As the fisher crossed the bridge, they shook the log so hard that he fell into the water. On the riverbank, the people who had been fooled laughed and laughed. Then they went to the market, sold their goods, and ate a fine fish dinner that night!

Name _____

1. How are topics of the folktales similar and/or different?

_____

_____

_____

2. How are the patterns of events in the folktales similar and/or different?

_____

_____

_____

3. How are the themes of the folktales similar and/or different?

_____

_____

_____

_____

Standard
1

Lesson A
Use Details and Examples

When reading informational text, it is important to **recall** explicit examples from text so that you can understand the most important details and events of the selection. In addition to recalling specific examples from text to answer basic comprehension questions, you can also use details and examples to make **inferences**.

When you make inferences, you use what you've read in addition to what you already know to fill in information that is not stated in a selection. You can use inferences to better understand a text and answer questions about it. To make inferences, ask yourself what information is missing from a text. Then think about your own experiences and other texts you've read to help you answer these questions. Here is a helpful visual to show you how inferring works:

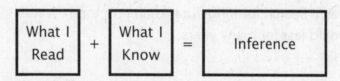

Note the kinds of inferences that you might make while reading nonfiction text.

I will read...	I might make inferences about...
Biography/ Autobiography	the subject's actions, events, the author's message
Informational Text	causes and effects, problems and solutions
Persuasive Text	the author's message, ideas used to support the author's message

Now look at the model for making inferences from a passage of informational text.

Use Details and Examples: Model

Read the selection below.

> Thousands of years ago, pharaohs ruled the great kingdom of Egypt. When pharaohs died, they were buried in tombs with their treasures. One of these pharaohs was very young. His name was King Tutankhamen (TOOT-ahngk-ah-muhn).
>
> The entrance to Tutankhamen's tomb was well hidden. The Egyptians built tombs that were hard to find and even harder to enter. They made secret entrances and false passages.
>
> Soon after the king was buried, robbers broke into the tomb and took some of the treasures. The tomb was then resealed. It stayed buried in the sand for thousands of years.
>
> In the early 1900s, an Englishman named Lord Carnarvon began the search for this pharoah's tomb. Carnarvon believed that the king was buried in the Valley of the Kings.
>
> In 1907, Carnarvon began working with a man named Howard Carter. Carter was an artist for paleontologists. He made drawings of the fossils and other findings. Carter and Carnarvon began a search for King Tutankhamen's tomb. It was a search that would last for many years.

- One way to know whether you understand a text is to **recall** details to answer basic questions. You can do this by recalling explicit details and examples from the selection to support your answer. For example, what happened to pharaohs after they died? Read the passage, and identify the text evidence that supports your answer.

Thousands of years ago, pharaohs ruled the great kingdom of Egypt. <u>When pharaohs died, they were buried in tombs with their treasures</u>. One of these pharaohs was very young. His name was King Tutankhamen (TOOT-ahngk-ah-muhn).

The entrance to Tutankhamen's tomb was well hidden. The Egyptians built tombs that were hard to find and even harder to enter. They made secret entrances and false passages.

Soon after the king was buried, robbers broke into the tomb and took some of the treasures. The tomb was then resealed. It stayed buried in the sand for thousands of years.

In the early 1900s, an Englishman named Lord Carnarvon began the search for this pharoah's tomb. Carnarvon believed that the king was buried in the Valley of the Kings.

In 1907, Carnarvon began working with a man named Howard Carter. Carter was an artist for paleontologists. He made drawings of the fossils and other findings. Carter and Carnarvon began a search for King Tutankhamen's tomb. It was a search that would last for many years.

- The underlined text states that when pharaohs died, they were buried in tombs with their treasures.

- In informational text, **cause and effect** clues as well as **problem and solution** clues can often help the reader to make an inference. Clues that can help you make inferences are underlined on page 84. For a reminder of how to identify these clues, go to 2.2 Lesson C **Describe Text Structure** on Volume 1 page 119.

Thousands of years ago, pharaohs ruled the great kingdom of Egypt. When pharaohs died, they were buried in tombs with their treasures. One of these pharaohs was very young. His name was King Tutankhamen (TOOT-ahngk-ah-muhn).

The entrance to Tutankhamen's tomb was well hidden. The Egyptians built tombs that were hard to find and even harder to enter. They made secret entrances and false passages.

Soon after the king was buried, robbers broke into the tomb and took some of the treasures. The tomb was then resealed. It stayed buried in the sand for thousands of years.

In the early 1900s, an Englishman named Lord Carnarvon began the search for this pharoah's tomb. Carnarvon believed that the king was buried in the Valley of the Kings.

In 1907, Carnarvon began working with a man named Howard Carter. Carter was an artist for paleontologists. He made drawings of the fossils and other findings. Carter and Carnarvon began a search for King Tutankhamen's tomb. It was a search that would last for many years.

- Once you've gathered clues from the story, you should think about your own experiences to help you make an inference from the text clues. Then you can make a connection that leads to an inference.

• Look at the chart on the following page. See how the clues from the text go in the left column, **What I Read**. The middle column, **What I Know**, has examples of personal experiences related to a text clue. These might help you make an inference. The right column, **Inference**, shows examples of inferences that might be made by using text clues and personal experiences.

What I Read	What I Know	Inference
The Egyptians built tombs that were hard to find and even harder to enter. They made secret entrances and false passages.	I keep my journal hidden in a box and locked in a drawer because I don't want to share my feelings with everyone.	The Egyptians did not want anybody to find King Tut.
The tomb was then resealed. It stayed buried in the sand for thousands of years.	When I lose something at the beach, it is hard to relocate.	The tomb stayed hidden because the sand burial provided protection.
Carter made drawings of the fossils and other findings.	On the news, they often show sketches of people they hope the public can help find.	Carter made the drawings so he would know what to look for when he was searching.

Now turn to pages 86–87 to practice using details and examples to make inferences.

Name _____

Use Details and Examples

Practice

Read the following story. Write your answers on the lines and in the chart.

> Coretta Scott King never planned on being a civil rights leader. She thought she would become a teacher or a singer. Instead, she became a leader in the fight for equal rights.
>
> Coretta Scott was born in 1927 in a small town in Alabama. She walked three miles to get to school each morning. And she walked three miles back each afternoon. Every day she watched school buses drive white children to their school.
>
> In those days segregation was the law in the South. African Americans could not go to certain restaurants. They could not drink from certain water fountains. They had to sit in the back of public buses. Black children and white children went to separate schools.
>
> Coretta's father Obadiah (oh-buh-DIGH-uh) was the first African American in his county to own his own truck. Some white truckers felt that he was taking away their business. One day the Scotts came home from church to find that their home had burned down.

1. Where and when was Coretta Scott King born? Use text evidence in your answer.

_____

_____

Name _____

2. Use this chart to help you find explicit examples and details from text to make inferences. Remember that…

| What I Read | + | What I Know | = | Inference |

What I Read	What I Know	Inference

Standard
2

Lesson B

Determine Main Idea and Supporting Details

The **main idea** of a passage tells you what it is mostly about. The **supporting details** help you understand the main idea.

Here's a model of determining main idea and supporting details.

Determine Main Idea and Supporting Details: Model

Read the passage below.

> Many newborn rattlesnakes do not survive their first year of life. A baby rattlesnake is only about ten inches long. Although baby rattlesnakes have short fangs and a poisonous bite, they are often eaten by birds and animals. The adult rattlesnakes do not raise their young. The young snakes are entirely on their own. Many die of hunger. In the winter, they die if they do not find a warm place where they can hibernate.

What is the main idea?

To identify the main idea, ask yourself: *What is this passage mostly about?* The main idea of this passage is underlined below.

> Many newborn rattlesnakes do not survive their first year of life. A baby rattlesnake is only about ten inches long. Although baby rattlesnakes have short fangs and a poisonous bite, they are often eaten by birds and animals. The adult rattlesnakes do not raise their young. The young snakes are entirely on their own. Many die of hunger. In the winter, they die if they do not find a warm place where they can hibernate.

The main idea of his passage is that many newborn rattlesnakes do not survive their first year of life. As in this example, the main idea often appears at or near the beginning of a passage.

Common Core State Standards Literacy Handbook

What are the supporting details?

Each supporting detail is connected to the main idea. A supporting detail gives an example or a reason why. To identify supporting details, ask yourself: *Why don't newborn rattlesnakes survive their first year of life?*

Supporting Detail 1

One supporting detail is underlined below.

> Many newborn rattlesnakes do not survive their first year of life. A baby rattlesnake is only about ten inches long. Although baby rattlesnakes have short fangs and a poisonous bite, <u>they are often eaten by birds and animals</u>. The adult rattlesnakes do not raise their young. The young snakes are entirely on their own. Many die of hunger. In the winter, they die if they do not find a warm place where they can hibernate.

One reason that many newborn rattlesnakes do not survive their first year of life is that they are often eaten by birds and animals.

Supporting Detail 2

> Many newborn rattlesnakes do not survive their first year of life. A baby rattlesnake is only about ten inches long. Although baby rattlesnakes have short fangs and a poisonous bite, they are often eaten by birds and animals. The adult rattlesnakes do not raise their young. The young snakes are entirely on their own. <u>Many die of hunger</u>. In the winter, they die if they do not find a warm place where they can hibernate.

Another reason that many newborn rattlesnakes do not survive their first year of life is that they die of hunger.

Supporting Detail 3

Many newborn rattlesnakes do not survive their first year of life. A baby rattlesnake is only about ten inches long. Although baby rattlesnakes have short fangs and a poisonous bite, they are often eaten by birds and animals. The adult rattlesnakes do not raise their young. The young snakes are entirely on their own. Many die of hunger. <u>In the winter, they die if they do not find a warm place where they can hibernate.</u>

Another reason that many newborn rattlesnakes do not survive their first year of life is that they cannot find a warm place to hibernate.

Now turn to page 91 to practice determining main idea and supporting details.

Common Core State Standards Literacy Handbook

Name _____

Determine Main Idea and Supporting Details

Practice

Read the passage below. Identify the <u>main idea</u>, or what the passage is mostly about. Then identify the <u>supporting details</u> that explain or tell more about the main idea.

> Millions of people visit national parks each year. Some park officials worry that large numbers of visitors will cause damage to the parks. People who walk in the park trample plants and soil, causing erosion. As people drive through the parks, their cars put out harmful chemicals that may damage plant life. At one park, pine tree needles are turning yellow. Park officials at another park believe that animals may be moving away from their homes and feeding grounds due to noise from helicopters and airplanes.

1. Circle the main idea in the passage above.

2. Underline a supporting detail in the passage.

3. Underline another supporting detail in the passage.

4. Underline another supporting detail in the passage.

2

Lesson C
Summarize

In this lesson you will learn how to use the main idea and supporting details in order to **summarize** the selection. When you summarize, you use your own words to tell the most important ideas in a selection. Summarizing helps you understand and remember what you've read.

Now look at a model of how to summarize.

Summarize: Model

Reread the selection below. Then see how to use the main idea and supporting details in order to write a summary.

> Many newborn rattlesnakes do not survive their first year of life. A baby rattlesnake is only about ten inches long. Although baby rattlesnakes have short fangs and a poisonous bite, they are often eaten by birds and animals. The adult rattlesnakes do not raise their young. The young snakes are entirely on their own. Many die of hunger. In the winter, they die if they do not find a warm place where they can hibernate.

Main Idea:

Many newborn rattlesnakes do not survive their first year of life.

This idea is what the passage is mostly about. It appears at the beginning of the selection.

Supporting Detail 1:

They are eaten by birds and animals.

This detail gives a reason why many newborn rattlesnakes do not survive their first year of life.

Supporting Detail 2:

Many die of hunger.

This detail gives another reason why many newborn rattlesnakes do not survive their first year of life.

Supporting Detail 3:

In the winter, they die if they do not find a warm place where they can hibernate.

This detail gives another reason why many newborn rattlesnakes do not survive their first year of life.

Summary:

Many newborn rattlesnakes do not survive their first year of life because they are eaten by animals, die of hunger, or do not find a warm place to hibernate.

This summary explains why many newborn rattlesnakes do not survive their first year of life. The writer of the summary uses his or her own words to summarize the most important ideas in the selection.

Now turn to page 94 to practice summarizing.

Name _____

Summarize

Practice

1. Read the selection below.

2. Identify the most important ideas in the selection. First identify the main idea, or what the selection is mostly about. Then identify the details that explain or tell more about the main idea.

3. Use the important ideas you listed to write a summary of the selection. Remember to use your own words.

4. Write your answers.

> Arbor Day is a special day that people around the world celebrate by planting trees. People plant trees on Arbor Day for many reasons. They plant them to make their surroundings more beautiful and to replace trees that have died or been cut down. Some people plant trees to remember loved ones who have passed away. Others plant trees to fight global warming.

1. Circle the main idea in the passage.

2. Underline a supporting detail in the passage.

3. Underline another supporting detail in the passage.

4. Underline another supporting detail in the passage.

5. Write a summary:

_____

_____

_____

Lesson D
Read Historical Text

Historical text is informational text. That means it includes many facts and information about important **events.** The purpose for reading historical text differs from the purpose of reading a fictional text. Historical text is read to gain knowledge of a particular era, and how it shaped the future.

Understanding the events within a historic text can be done with a variety of strategies. One of the most useful strategies is determining **cause and effect.** This strategy allows the reader to understand what happened and why something happened, by using specific information in the text.

Now look at a model for explaining historical text.

Historical Text: Model

At one time, African Americans in the United States did not have the same rights as white people. They had separate schools, and public places, such as restaurants, often had whites-only spaces. In the South Atlantic states, this segregation was common, but people worked together to change it.

A turning point came one day in 1955, when an African American woman named Rosa Parks would not give up her bus seat to a white person in Montgomery, Alabama. As a result, she was arrested. Martin Luther King, Jr., encouraged all African Americans to stop riding the bus. A year later, the city of Montgomery decided to make segregated buses illegal.

Dr. King asked African Americans to disobey the rules of segregation quietly. In North Carolina in 1960, African American college students sat at a whites-only lunch counter. They stayed until it closed.

Because people worked together, things changed. On a warm day in 1963, at least 200,000 people joined together to march on Washington, D.C. Dr. King gave a powerful speech about his dream of all colors of people living freely together, and the government listened. Change happened slowly, but by the 1970s, legal segregation had disappeared.

When discussing particular **events** in **history**, these events are often presented in chronological order, as in the selection on the previous page. Sometimes one event is a cause for another event. Most historic texts will use clue words that signal **cause and effect**. Here are some clue words: *so that*, *since*, *because*, *if*, *reason*, *why*, and *as a result*. Examples of cause/effect clue words in this selection are underlined below.

> At one time, African Americans in the United States did not have the same rights as white people. They had separate schools, and public places, such as restaurants, often had whites-only spaces. In the South Atlantic states, this segregation was common, but people worked together to change it.
>
> A turning point came one day in 1955, when an African American woman named Rosa Parks would not give up her bus seat to a white person in Montgomery, Alabama. <u>As a result</u>, she was arrested. Martin Luther King, Jr., encouraged all African Americans to stop riding the bus. A year later, the city of Montgomery decided to make segregated buses illegal.
>
> Dr. King asked African Americans to disobey the rules of segregation quietly. In North Carolina in 1960, African American college students sat at a whites-only lunch counter. They stayed until it closed.
>
> <u>Because</u> people worked together, things changed. On a warm day in 1963, at least 200,000 people joined together to march on Washington, D.C. Dr. King gave a powerful speech about his dream of all colors of people living freely together, and the government listened. Change happened slowly, but by the 1970s, legal segregation had disappeared.

After locating signal words within a text, you should be able to determine the cause and effect from the surrounding text. Look at the text surrounding the signal words in the selection and try to determine the cause and effect of the event.

At one time, African Americans in the United States did not have the same rights as white people. They had separate schools, and public places, such as restaurants, often had whites-only spaces. In the South Atlantic states, this segregation was common, but people worked together to change it.

A turning point came one day in 1955, when an African American woman named Rosa Parks would not give up her bus seat to a white person in Montgomery, Alabama. As a result, she was arrested. Martin Luther King, Jr., encouraged all African Americans to stop riding the bus. A year later, the city of Montgomery decided to make segregated buses illegal.

Dr. King asked African Americans to disobey the rules of segregation quietly. In North Carolina in 1960, African American college students sat at a whites-only lunch counter. They stayed until it closed.

Because people worked together, things changed. On a warm day in 1963, at least 200,000 people joined together to march on Washington, D.C. Dr. King gave a powerful speech about his dream of all colors of people living freely together, and the government listened. Change happened slowly, but by the 1970s, legal segregation had disappeared.

Cause	Effect
Rosa Parks would not give up her bus seat to a white person in Montgomery, Alabama	she was arrested
people worked together	things changed

Sometimes a text won't have explicit clue words signaling a cause/effect relationship, so you will need to read each sentence carefully to determine if a cause/effect relationship exists. You can do this by using your prior knowledge and asking yourself if it makes sense that an event could cause a particular action. For example, in the sentence, "In the late 1880s, more people wanted to move to the United States to escape poverty in Europe," you should recognize the cause/effect relationship. Escaping poverty is a reason to seek a life in a new country. More examples of cause/effect relationships in the selection are underlined on page 98.

At one time, African Americans in the United States did not have the same rights as white people. They had separate schools, and public places, such as restaurants, often had whites-only spaces. In the South Atlantic states, this segregation was common, but people worked together to change it.

A turning point came one day in 1955, when an African American woman named Rosa Parks would not give up her bus seat to a white person in Montgomery, Alabama. As a result, she was arrested. Martin Luther King, Jr., encouraged all African Americans to stop riding the bus. A year later, the city of Montgomery decided to make segregated buses illegal.

Dr. King asked African Americans to disobey the rules of segregation quietly. In North Carolina in 1960, African American college students sat at a whites-only lunch counter. They stayed until it closed.

Because people worked together, things changed. On a warm day in 1963, at least 200,000 people joined together to march on Washington, D.C. Dr. King gave a powerful speech about his dream of all colors of people living freely together, and the government listened. Change happened slowly, but by the 1970s, legal segregation had disappeared.

Cause	Effect
Rosa Parks would not give up her bus seat to a white person in Montgomery, Alabama	she was arrested
people worked together	things changed
Martin Luther King, Jr., encouraged all African Americans to stop riding the bus.	A year later, the city of Montgomery decided to make segregated buses illegal.
Dr. King asked African Americans to disobey the rules of segregation quietly.	In North Carolina in 1960, African American college students sat at a whites-only lunch counter.
Dr. King gave a powerful speech about his dream of all colors of people living freely together; change happened	the government listened; by the 1970s, legal segregation had disappeared

Now turn to pages 99–100 to practice explaining historical text.

Common Core State Standards Literacy Handbook

Name _____

Read Historical Text

Practice

Read the following selection. Then write your answers.

> In the early 1800s, the United States needed room to grow. Most people lived in the East. The cities were crowded. Because new land was expensive, young families couldn't afford to buy farms.
>
> Then the United States government purchased land from France. The government also acquired land from Mexico. As a result, the country soon stretched all the way to the Pacific Ocean. People looked to the setting sun with outstretched arms and said, "Go west!"
>
> Settlers rode in wagons or on horses. They followed long, dusty trails across hot plains for thousands of miles. There was no shelter, so people slept in tents on the ground. They had to watch out for wild animals like wolves and snakes. The trip west could take months.
>
> Then a railroad was built that stretched from the East Coast almost to the West Coast. The railroad made travel faster. More people poured into the new lands. The settlers quickly built small towns where the farming, fishing, and mining were good.

1. Circle or underline the cause and effect clue words in the selection.

Name _____

Read the selection carefully to look for cause and effect relationships that aren't signaled by a clue word.

2. Use the chart below to list as many cause/effect relationships as you can.

Cause	Effect

Lesson E
Read Scientific Text

Scientific text is informational text. That means it includes many facts, ideas, concepts, and procedures. The purpose for reading scientific text differs from the purpose for reading a fictional text. Scientific text is read to gain knowledge in a particular area of science.

Understanding the concepts and ideas within a scientific text can be done with a variety of strategies. One of the most useful strategies is determining **cause and effect**. This strategy allows the reader to understand what happened, and why it happened, by using specific information in the text.

Now look at a model for explaining scientific text.

Read Scientific Text: Model
Read the selection below.

You do not feel it, but Earth moves. It rotates around an axis, which is an imaginary line through the center of Earth. It takes 24 hours, or one day, for Earth to rotate one time. As Earth rotates, half of it faces the sun and has day. The other side has night. As Earth continues to rotate, the light side becomes dark. The dark side becomes light. The cycle of day and night repeats every 24 hours.

As Earth rotates, it also revolves around the sun. Because Earth's axis is tilted, the sun hits Earth at different angles. Each of Earth's hemispheres, or halves, gets different amounts of sunlight. The tilt of Earth's axis and Earth's revolution around the sun cause the four seasons.

As Earth rotates on its axis around the sun, Earth's hemispheres get more or less sunlight. In June the North Pole tilts toward the sun and the South Pole tilts away from it. It is summer in the Northern Hemisphere and winter in the Southern Hemisphere. In December the North Pole tilts away from the sun and the South Pole tilts toward it. It is winter in the Northern Hemisphere and summer in the Southern Hemisphere.

- When discussing why something happens in a particular way, most **scientific texts** will use clue words that signal **cause and effect**. Here are some clue words: *so that, since, because, reason, why, cause,* and *as a result.* Examples of cause/effect clue words in this text are underlined below.

> You do not feel it, but Earth moves. It rotates around an axis, which is an imaginary line through the center of Earth. It takes 24 hours, or one day, for Earth to rotate one time. As Earth rotates, half of it faces the sun and has day. The other side has night. As Earth continues to rotate, the light side becomes dark. The dark side becomes light. The cycle of day and night repeats every 24 hours.
>
> As Earth rotates, it also revolves around the sun. <u>Because</u> Earth's axis is tilted, the sun hits Earth at different angles. Each of Earth's hemispheres, or halves, gets different amounts of sunlight. The tilt of Earth's axis and Earth's revolution around the sun <u>cause</u> the four seasons.
>
> As Earth rotates on its axis around the sun, Earth's hemispheres get more or less sunlight. In June the North Pole tilts toward the sun and the South Pole tilts away from it. It is summer in the Northern Hemisphere and winter in the Southern Hemisphere. In December the North Pole tilts away from the sun and the South Pole tilts toward it. It is winter in the Northern Hemisphere and summer in the Southern Hemisphere.

- Locating signal words within a text can help you determine the cause and effect found in the surrounding text. Look at the text surrounding signal words, as underlined in the passage on page 103, to determine the cause and effect.

You do not feel it, but Earth moves. It rotates around an axis, which is an imaginary line through the center of Earth. It takes 24 hours, or one day, for Earth to rotate one time. As Earth rotates, half of it faces the sun and has day. The other side has night. As Earth continues to rotate, the light side becomes dark. The dark side becomes light. The cycle of day and night repeats every 24 hours.

As Earth rotates, it also revolves around the sun. Because Earth's axis is tilted, the sun hits Earth at different angles. Each of Earth's hemispheres, or halves, gets different amounts of sunlight. The tilt of Earth's axis and Earth's revolution around the sun cause the four seasons.

As Earth rotates on its axis around the sun, Earth's hemispheres get more or less sunlight. In June the North Pole tilts toward the sun and the South Pole tilts away from it. It is summer in the Northern Hemisphere and winter in the Southern Hemisphere. In December the North Pole tilts away from the sun and the South Pole tilts toward it. It is winter in the Northern Hemisphere and summer in the Southern Hemisphere.

Cause	Effect
the Earth's axis is tilted	the sun hits Earth at different angles
the tilt of the Earth's axis and the Earth's revolution around the sun	four seasons

- Sometimes a text won't have explicit clue words signaling a cause/effect relationship, so you will need to read each sentence carefully to determine if a cause/effect relationship exists. You can do this by using your prior knowledge, and asking yourself if it makes sense that one action caused another. For example, in the sentence, "April showers bring May flowers," you should recognize that plants need rain to grow, so this sentence shows a cause/effect relationship. The rain in April caused the flowers to grow in May. Now try finding more examples of cause/effect relationships in the underlined text on page 104.

You do not feel it, but Earth moves. It rotates around an axis, which is an imaginary line through the center of Earth. It takes 24 hours, or one day, for Earth to rotate one time. As Earth rotates, half of it faces the sun and has day. The other side has night. As Earth continues to rotate, the light side becomes dark. The dark side becomes light. The cycle of day and night repeats every 24 hours.

As Earth rotates, it also revolves around the sun. Because Earth's axis is tilted, the sun hits Earth at different angles. Each of Earth's hemispheres, or halves, gets different amounts of sunlight. The tilt of Earth's axis and Earth's revolution around the sun cause the four seasons.

As Earth rotates on its axis around the sun, Earth's hemispheres get more or less sunlight. In June the North Pole tilts toward the sun and the South Pole tilts away from it. It is summer in the Northern Hemisphere and winter in the Southern Hemisphere. In December the North Pole tilts away from the sun and the South Pole tilts toward it. It is winter in the Northern Hemisphere and summer in the Southern Hemisphere.

Cause	Effect
the Earth's axis is tilted	the sun hits Earth at different angles
the tilt of the Earth's axis and the Earth's revolution around the sun	four seasons
Earth continues to rotate	the light side becomes dark
In June the North Pole tilts toward the sun and the South Pole tilts away from it.	It is summer in the Northern Hemisphere and winter in the Southern Hemisphere.
In December the North Pole tilts away from the sun and the South Pole tilts toward it.	It is winter in the Northern Hemisphere and summer in the Southern Hemisphere.

Now turn to pages 105–106 to practice explaining scientific text.

Name _____

Read Scientific Text

Practice

Read the following selection. Then write your answers.

> Tornadoes begin with warm, humid air. Humid air is air that holds a lot of moisture. This humid air meets up with colder air. As the air masses come together, the warm air rises. As the warm air moves upward, it holds more and more moisture. Huge, dark clouds called thunderheads begin to develop. These clouds can spread as wide as 100 miles (161 km) across the sky. There is so much moisture in the clouds that it can't just evaporate into the air. So it falls as rain. The thunderheads produce giant storms with thunder and lightning. These storms are called supercells.
>
> Winds high up in the storm clouds blow faster than the winds lower down. The winds also blow in different directions. This causes the air to spin. Then, as the winds spin, they form a long funnel cloud. However, one last thing needs to happen for the funnel cloud to become a tornado. It needs to touch the ground.

1. Circle or underline the cause and effect clue words in the selection.

Name _____

Read the selection carefully to look for cause and effect relationships that aren't signaled by a clue word.

2. Use the chart below to list as many cause/effect relationships as you can.

Cause	Effect

Lesson F

Read Technical Text

Technical text is one type of informational text.

- Technical text is read for the purpose of learning more about a subject or understanding how to complete a task.

- Technical texts are often accompanied by charts, diagrams, illustrations, and other visual elements that support the text and provide additional information about the subject.

Directions are one type of technical text.

- Common types of directions are user guides, recipes, and how-to texts that help people build ant farms or construct model airplanes.

- Information in directions is often presented as a series of steps in a procedure. These steps may be supported and enhanced by a chart, diagram, illustration, or other visual element.

- A person performs the steps in sequence while looking at the visual element in order to build the ant farm or construct the model airplane.

If the person understands the connections between the steps and between the text and the visual element, then he or she is more likely to successfully complete the task.

Now look at a model of how to understand and explain steps in a procedure.

Read Technical Text: Model

Read the directions and look at the photographs below. As you read, focus on what happens, when it happens, and why it happens.

How to Make Sugar Crystals

1. Wash your hands with soap and water.
2. Ask an adult to help you pour 1 cup of hot water into a glass jar.
3. Stir 3 cups of sugar into the water.
4. Stir in food coloring.
5. Wet a thick cotton string and roll it in some sugar. This will give the crystals something to stick to. Let it dry.
6. Tie the string to the middle of a pencil. Place the pencil over the jar and let the string hang into the liquid.
7. Wait 2–3 days until the crystals have stopped growing on the string.
8. Carefully pull the string out and wait for it to dry.

Before   **After**

What task do these directions tell you how to do?
The directions tell you how to make sugar crystals.

How do you know the correct order in which to do the steps?
The steps in a procedure are often numbered to tell the reader the order in which things should be done. However, some procedures contain sequence words, such as *first, then, next,* and *last,* to help the reader follow the steps in the correct order. As you can see, the steps in this example are numbered for you.

What should happen *before* you make the crystals?
You should wash your hands.

What should happen *as* you make the crystals?
You should pour hot water into a jar and add sugar and food coloring. Then you should roll some string in sugar, tie the string to a pencil, and place the pencil on top of the jar so that the string hangs into the liquid.

What should happen *after* you make the crystals?
You should wait a few days for the crystals to grow and then pull the string out and wait for it to dry.

What would happen if you skipped Step 4?
If you skipped Step 4, the crystals would not have any color.

What would happen if you skipped Step 7?
If you skipped Step 7, you might not have as many crystals.

What additional information do the photographs provide?
The "Before" photograph shows about how much string to use and how far down to hang it in the jar. The "After" photograph shows what the crystals should look like before you remove the string from the jar.

Now turn to pages 110–111 to practice understanding and explaining the steps in a procedure.

Name _____

Read Technical Text

Practice

Read the following directions and answer the questions on the following page.
Write your answers on the lines.

How to Build an Ant Farm

1: Place a cardboard tube in a large jar. The tube makes the ants tunnel near the side of the jar so that you can see them.

2: Fill the jar with soil and sand.

3: Find an ant colony in your yard or a park. Catch at least 20 ants from the same colony to put in your farm.

4: Try to find a queen ant. Queen ants are usually larger than the other ants. Some queen ants have wings.

5: Place the ants carefully in the jar.

6. Cover the top of the jar with cloth. Use a rubber band to hold the cloth in place.

7: Feed the ants once a week. Ants can eat tiny bits of food.

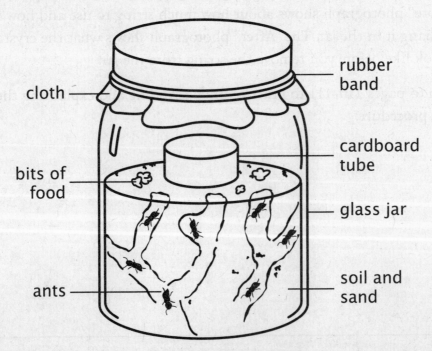

cloth

rubber band

cardboard tube

glass jar

bits of food

soil and sand

ants

Name _____

1. What task do these directions tell you how to do?

_____

2. How do you know the correct order in which to do the steps?

_____

3. What should happen *before* you get the ants?

_____

4. What should happen *as* you get the ants?

_____

5. What should happen *after* you get the ants?

_____

6. What would happen if you skipped Step 1?

_____

_____

7. What would happen if you skipped Step 6?

_____

_____

8. Why should you do Step 2 before you do Step 5?

_____

_____

9. What additional information does the diagram provide about how to place the cardboard tube?

_____

_____

Standard
4

2

Lesson A
Understand Precise Vocabulary

Writers use precise, or exact, language and specific content vocabulary when providing important information about their topics. For example, the social studies word *expedition* better describes the journey that explorers go on instead of *trip*. The word *expedition* implies there are explorers going somewhere with a purpose such as exploration or for battle. The word *trip* is a general term that could describe an adventure or just a vacation.

Sometimes, as you are reading, you come across a precise vocabulary word that is unfamiliar. When this happens, you can often look in the text for context clues. Context clues are words, sentences, or images that help a reader determine or clarify the meaning of an unfamiliar word.

Now look at a model of how to use context clues.

Understand Precise Vocabulary: Model

Read the examples below to help you understand context clues.

> The Great Plains is a large area of flat land that runs through the middle of the United States. In the Midwest Region the Dakotas, Nebraska, and Kansas are part of the Great Plains. Here, the climate and rich soil make it ideal for farming. Winters can be frigid and dry. Summers are hot. This climate is good for growing crops. In the Dakotas and Kansas, farmers grow wheat. The Great Plains includes part of the Corn Belt. Most of the corn grown in the United States grows here. The Midwest uses its land well.

At first glance, *frigid* seems like a difficult word. But if you keep reading, you figure out that winters in the Midwest are being compared to the summers. If the summers are hot, the winters must be cold. Therefore, *frigid* must mean cold.

The Midwest continued to flourish, or do well. More settlers pushed on to the Great Plains. The land near the Mississippi River was already settled, so the new settlers had to move farther west. From there it was hard for them to get their goods to market. When the railroads came that problem was solved. Small villages, such as Dodge City and Abilene in Kansas, became major railroad towns. Railroads connected the new settlers to these towns so they could sell their goods.

Flourish is another difficult word. By reading on, you learn that *flourish* means "to do well." The writer could have used the word "grow," but the term *flourish* is more appropriate to describe that the Midwest didn't only become larger; it also began to succeed economically.

Now turn to pages 114–115 to practice using context clues to determine the meaning of other precise words.

Name _____

Understand Precise Vocabulary

Practice

Read the paragraph below. Then write the meaning of each word in dark type and the context clues that helped you figure out its meaning. Write your answers on the lines.

> The **audience streamed** into the theater to hear Regina Jackson's talk. Hundreds of people moved smoothly but quickly into their seats. Jackson was the world's leading **authority** on jaguars. No one else knew more than she did about the lives of these big cats. From the moment she began to speak, everyone sat quietly. You could see by their interested expressions that they were **fascinated** by what she had to say. When Regina finished, everyone stood up and began to applaud.

1. audience Definition:

_____

_____

Context clues:

_____

_____

2. streamed Definition:

_____

_____

Context clues:

_____

_____

Name _____

3. authority Definition:

_____

_____

Context clues:

_____

_____

_____

4. fascinated Definition:

_____

_____

Context clues:

_____

_____

Lesson B

Understand Content Words

Sometimes you come across an unfamiliar word that is not frequently used because it is specific to a topic or subject area. For example, the word *peninsula* is a term you would probably only use when talking about the geography of a certain place.

When you come across unfamiliar content words, you can often look in the text for context clues. Context clues are words, sentences, or images that help a reader determine or clarify the meaning of an unfamiliar word.

Now look at a model of how to use context clues.

Context Clues to Understand Content Words: Model

Read the examples below to help you understand context clues.

> In college Copernicus spent long hours learning as much about astronomy as he could. He read many ancient texts that were written in Greek and Latin. He found that some scientists of long ago had different ideas about the way the planets and the sun were positioned in the sky.
>
> One book that Copernicus discovered described the beliefs of an ancient Greek astronomer named Aristarchus. He taught that the planets and the sun do not revolve around Earth. Rather, Aristarchus said, all the planets—including Earth—revolve around the sun. This belief is called the heliocentric theory.

At first glance, *astronomy* seems like a difficult word. But if you keep reading, you soon learn that *astronomy* is the study of the planets and other objects in the sky.

Heliocentric is another difficult word that is specific to the topic of astronomy. By reading for context clues, you can figure out that *heliocentric* refers to the idea that the planets revolve around the sun, just as the astronomer Aristarchus believed.

Now turn to pages 117–118 to practice using context clues to determine the meaning of other content words.

Name _____

Understand Content Words

Practice

Read the paragraph below. Then write the meaning of each word in dark type and the context clues that helped you figure out its meaning. Write your answers on the lines.

> All living things need energy to survive. Where do they get that energy? From their food! Plants can make their own food by using air, water, and the energy from the sun. Plants are called producers because they produce, or make their own energy.
>
> Animals cannot make their own energy as plants do. They must consume food to get energy. Animals are called consumers. **Herbivores, carnivores,** and **omnivores** are types of consumers. Animals that eat only plants are called herbivores. The mule deer is one of the herbivores that lives in the Rocky Mountains.
>
> Carnivores and omnivores are predators. They must hunt for food to eat. Carnivores eat meat. A snake is one example of a carnivore. It eats worms, caterpillars, frogs, mice, fish, and small birds. Omnivores, such as a small bird, eat insects, spiders, and the seeds of plants.

1. herbivore definition:

_____

_____

Context clues:

_____

_____

Name _____

2. carnivore definition:

_____

_____

Context clues:

_____

_____

3. omnivore definition:

_____

_____

Context clues:

_____

_____

Lesson C

Describe Text Structure

When you understand the way an author has organized the text, you are better able to understand that text. Authors make choices about how they present the information in a text based on what they have to say. This organization is called text structure.

In this lesson, you will learn more about these four ways informational text is organized as well as signal words that help you identify each text structure. Signal words provide hints that help you make sense of what you are reading. Certain signal words are associated with each type of text structure.

- Chronological Text Structure
- Comparison and Contrast Text Structure
- Cause and Effect Text Structure
- Problem and Solution Text Structure

Chronological Text Structure

Authors sometimes organize their writing in chronological order. Chronological order is the order in which things happen. It is also called time order.

Read the paragraph below. Pay special attention to the underlined signal words. They help you understand the chronological order of events in the text.

> My family and I went to the Kennedy Space Center in Florida. The <u>first</u> thing we did when we got there was to take a tour of a space shuttle that once flew into space. <u>During</u> our tour, an astronaut showed us her spacesuit. I even got to try on the space boots. <u>Next</u>, we tasted the food astronauts eat while they are in space. It was really different from other foods that I had eaten but it tasted pretty good. <u>Finally</u>, we got in a special booth that showed us what it is like to be weightless! It was an amazing day.

The words *first*, *during*, *next*, and *finally* tell in what order the events happened. Therefore the text is structured chronologically.

Chronological Signal Words

Chronological signal words tell you there is an order to the events or ideas.

before
first
then
next
later

Comparison and Contrast Text Structure

Authors sometimes organize their writing by comparison and contrast. When you compare and contrast two or more people, places, events, or things, you find ways in which they are alike or different. Compare and contrast signal words such as *like, both, also, most, but, whereas,* and *however* may tell you things are being compared and contrasted.

Read the passage below. Notice the underlined signal words help you understand the comparison and contrast text structure.

> Babe Ruth and Lou Gehrig played together as New York Yankees in the 1920s and 1930s. The two teammates could not have been more different. Ruth played in the outfield. Gehrig played first base. Ruth was outgoing, whereas Gehrig was quiet. Ruth liked attention, but Gehrig was shy.
>
> Despite their differences, both players were known for hitting home runs. Ruth set several records for the number of home runs hit in a season. Gehrig also set a record by hitting four home runs in one game. Both Ruth and Gehrig are members of the Baseball Hall of Fame.

The words *whereas, but, both,* and *also* help to tell what is similar and different about the baseball players Babe Ruth and Lou Gehrig. Therefore, this text is structured using comparison and contrast.

Compare and Contrast Signal Words

Compare and contrast signal words tells you that two or more events or ideas are going to be compared.

    also
    on the other hand
    although
    but
    both
    whereas
    likewise

Cause and Effect Text Structure

Authors sometimes organize their writing by cause and effect. Signal words such as *because*, *since*, and *as a result* can help you determine what caused something to happen.

A **cause** is why something happens. To determine the cause, ask "Why did it happen?"

An **effect** is what happens. To determine the effect, ask "What happened?"

Read the passage below to help you understand the cause and effect text structure. Notice the underlined signal words. They provide hints that help you make sense of what you are reading.

> Sometimes humans change an ecosystem without meaning to. It's that way in my town, Oakville. Recently, many new homes were built in a wooded area of the city. People moved onto the land where deer and other wild animals lived. As a result, the only place the deer could roam was in the city. Early in the morning, it's not unusual to see deer walking down the middle of the main street. They wander in people's yards looking for plants to eat. It can be dangerous for drivers because the deer can run in front of cars.
>
> That's one reason our class has adopted the deer as a project. We're writing to ask city council to leave some wooded areas for the deer.

The words *as a result*, *because*, and *one reason* help to determine what caused something to happen. For example, when people moved onto the land where the deer lived, the result or effect was the deer started to roam in the city.

Another example is when the students write that they have adopted the deer as a project, they state that one reason is because the deer can run in front of cars. The fact that the deer or drivers can be harmed was one cause for adopting the deer as a project. Therefore this passage uses the cause and effect text structure to present ideas.

Cause and Effect Signal Words
because
thus
for this reason
in order to
if . . . then

Problem and Solution Text Structure

Authors sometimes organize their writing by problem and solution. The author will present a problem that needs to be solved. A problem can be between individuals or groups, or it might be with something that is going on in the world. A problem might even occur with just one person. Identifying the problem and solution will help you understand the text better.

Read the passage on page 124. Notice how the underlined signal words help you understand the problem and solution text structure.

In the early 1800s, the United States needed room to grow.

The <u>problem</u> was most people lived in the East. The cities were crowded. New land was expensive. Young families couldn't afford to buy farms.

Then, as a <u>solution</u>, the United States government purchased land from France. The government also acquired land from Mexico. Soon the country stretched all the way to the Pacific Ocean. People looked to the setting sun with outstretched arms and said, "Go west!"

Settlers rode in wagons or on horses. They followed long, dusty trails across hot plains for thousands of miles. There was no shelter. People slept in tents on the ground. They had to watch out for wild animals like wolves and snakes. The trip west could take months.

Then a railroad was built that stretched from the East Coast almost to the West Coast. The railroad made travel faster. More people poured into the new lands. The settlers quickly built small towns where the farming, fishing, and mining were good.

The word *problem* appears in the first paragraph and indicates that the cities in the eastern United States were crowded and land was expensive. The solution follows the problem and is indicated by the word *solution* in the second paragraph. The United States government acquired more land to the west and people built small towns on this new land.

Problem and Solution Signal Words

the problem
resolved
the solution

Now turn to pages 125–126 to practice identifying text structures.

Name _____

Describe Text Structure

Practice

Read the passages below. Describe the text structure the writer uses in each passage. Identify any signal words that help you determine the structure. Write your answers on the lines.

> Beep Baseball is a lot like baseball. They both use a ball and bases, and both have two teams. The players use a bat to hit the ball.
>
> Unlike players on baseball teams, the players on Beep Baseball teams are sighted and non-sighted people. The sport is played with a big ball and a big bat. There are only two bases, which look like soft towers.
>
> When a batter hits a ball, one of the bases begins to beep loudly. The batter runs toward the sound. If the batter can reach the base before someone throws a ball to the base, his or her team scores a point.

1. Text Structure: _____

2. Signal Words: _____

> The Plains Indians lived in North America before the Europeans came. Since they had no horses, the Plains Indians traveled on foot. To hunt buffalo, they would surround a herd and shoot the buffalo with bows and arrows.
>
> This changed when Spanish explorers came to North America and brought horses with them. Now the Plains Indians hunters were able to ride horses and follow buffalo over long distances. They carried tipis with them and set up camps. The hunters could kill buffalo and pull them back to camp using their horses.
>
> Later, guns again changed the way that Plains Indians hunted.

1. Text Structure: _____

2. Signal Words: _____

Name _____

Cumberland Gap National Park is under attack! A plant called kudzu threatens the park's ecosystem. Few animals eat kudzu, and it grows so fast it's been called "the vine that ate the South." It can grow a foot a night! It grows even after it has been dosed with herbicide, or plant killer. That's bad news for native plants and trees. Kudzu grows right over them. It takes the sunlight plants need to live. Bits of kudzu came to Cumberland stuck to truck tires. The trucks were there to build a road. Now park rangers cut kudzu back. They apply herbicide to the plant's huge root. They could bring in goats because goats eat kudzu. But goats also eat native plants. Solving the kudzu problem will be tricky.

1. Text Structure: _____

2. Signal Words: _____

The Hoover Dam brought the Colorado River under control. Because the dam created a reserve of water, the water was used to irrigate dry farmland. It was also used as a water supply by nearby cities and towns.

But the biggest benefit of Hoover Dam is its hydroelectric power. The Hoover Dam makes a huge amount of electricity. As a result, 1.3 million people in California, Nevada, and Arizona have power every year.

As an energy source, the Hoover Dam is clean and cheap to run. It does not pollute the air the way fossil fuels would. However, this huge dam has had some bad effects on the environment. The river can no longer carry rich soil to the lands it flooded. Fish and other wildlife have lost their homes. For this reason, the landscape of the area will never be the same.

But the Hoover Dam is here to stay. It is a modern wonder of the United States.

1. Text Structure: _____

2. Signal Words: _____

Common Core State Standards Literacy Handbook

Lesson D
Compare Perspectives

Like fictional text, informational text can be written from different points of view.

A **firsthand account** of an event or topic is based on an author's personal experience. The author uses pronouns such as *I*, *me*, and *we* to describe the event or topic. Diaries, autobiographies, and letters are considered to be firsthand accounts.

A **secondhand account** of an event or topic is based on an author's research, rather than personal experience. The author uses pronouns such as *he*, *she*, and *they* to describe the event or topic. Encyclopedia entries, biographies, and textbooks are considered to be secondhand accounts.

Here's a model of how to compare perspectives.

Compare Perspectives: Model

The passages that follow are two accounts of the same topic: the Oregon Trail. One is a firsthand account and one is a secondhand account. Can you tell which is which? Read each and then see how to compare and contrast them.

The Oregon Trail

In 1843, thousands of people began traveling across America to the open lands of the West. Most of these people followed a path known as the Oregon Trail. Pioneers set out from towns along the Missouri River in the Midwest. They made a 2,000-mile trek to their new homes in California and Oregon. Some traveled in covered wagons. Others were on foot or horseback. The route was filled with danger and hardship.

from Across the Plains in 1844

August 1st we nooned in a beautiful grove on the north side of the Platte [River]. We had by this time got used to climbing in and out of the wagon when in motion. When performing this feat that afternoon, my dress caught on an axle helve. I was thrown under the wagon wheel, which passed over and badly crushed my leg before my father could stop the team. He picked me up and saw the extent of the injury … The news soon spread along the train and a halt was called. A surgeon was found and the limb set …

Firsthand Account

Reread this passage. Pay special attention to the underlined words. These pronouns provide clues that this passage is a firsthand account.

from Across the Plains in 1844

August 1st we nooned in a beautiful grove on the north side of the Platte [River]. We had by this time got used to climbing in and out of the wagon when in motion. When performing this feat that afternoon, my dress caught on an axle helve. I was thrown under the wagon wheel, which passed over and badly crushed my leg before my father could stop the team. He picked me up and saw the extent of the injury … The news soon spread along the train and a halt was called. A surgeon was found and the limb set …

The author is a young girl telling about an actual experience she had on the Oregon trail. She uses the pronouns *we, I,* and *me* to describe the experience.

Secondhand Account

Now reread this passage. Pay special attention to the underlined pronoun. It is the clue that this is a secondhand account.

The Oregon Trail

In 1843, thousands of people began traveling across America to the open lands of the West. Most of these people followed a path known as the Oregon Trail. Pioneers set out from towns along the Missouri River in the Midwest. They made a 2,000-mile trek to their new homes in California and Oregon. Some traveled in covered wagons. Others were on foot or horseback. The route was filled with danger and hardship.

The author uses the pronoun *they*. This tells you that the author did not actually travel on the Oregon Trail. Instead, the author uses researched information to tell about the Oregon Trail.

Compare and Contrast

How are the accounts similar?

- Both are about the Oregon Trail.
- Both tell about the danger and hardship people experienced on the Oregon Trail.

How are the accounts different?

- The secondhand account focuses on broad, general information about the Oregon Trail. It *tells* readers that the route was dangerous.
- The firsthand account focuses on a single, specific experience that happened on the Oregon Trail. It *shows* readers that the route was dangerous by giving details about a particular person's journey on the trail.

Why read both?

- From the secondhand account, the reader gets more background information about what the Oregon Trail was.
- From the firsthand account, the reader gets a better understanding why it was so dangerous.

Now turn to pages 130–131 to practice comparing perspectives.

Name _____

Compare Perspectives

Practice

The passages that follow are two accounts of the life of Helen Keller. One is a firsthand account and one is a secondhand account. Read each passage and then answer the questions on the next page. Write your answers on the lines.

---

from *The Story of My Life*
by Helen Keller

Even in the days before my teacher came, I used to feel along the square stiff boxwood hedges, and, guided by the sense of smell would find the first violets and lilies. There, I went to find comfort and to hide my hot face in the cool leaves and grass.

What joy it was to lose myself in that garden of flowers.

Credit: Keller, Helen. The Story of My Life. 1905.

---

from *The Life of Helen Keller*

She felt her way along the bushes. She raised her head to catch the smell of the spring flowers. Often she would visit the garden and bury her face in the soft green leaves. It was a beautiful and peaceful place. Although she could not see, she knew the plants and flowers by touch.

It was one of her favorite places.

Name _____

1. Which passage is a firsthand account? How do you know?

   _____

   _____

   _____

2. Which passage is a secondhand account? How do you know?

   _____

   _____

   _____

3. Which account (firsthand or secondhand) tells readers more about Helen Keller's emotions in the garden?

   _____

4. Which account (firsthand or secondhand) explains why Helen Keller used her sense of touch to find the garden?

   _____

5. How do you think a reader might benefit from reading both accounts?

   _____

   _____

   _____

Lesson A

Interpret and Explain Visual Information

Visual information includes charts, graphs, time lines, diagrams, and web animations. Such information is useful for connecting key ideas in a text and explaining complex topics. Graphs, for example, can help you understand a large amount of information much more quickly, and sometimes more effectively, than written text alone.

In this lesson, you will learn more about how different kinds of visual information can increase your understanding of texts.

Graphs

A line graph is a good way to show how something changes over time. Points on the graph are connected by lines that make it easy to tell whether the occurrences of something increased or decreased as time passed.

Read the passage below and then look at the graph.

> The first residents of Utah were Native American hunters and gatherers. Later, other groups of Native Americans moved into the area, including the Ute, for whom the state was named. Two Spanish missionaries explored the area in 1776, but when "mountain men" James Bridger and Jedediah Smith arrived about 50 years later, they established trading posts and started a fur trade. In 1847 the Mormons began to arrive in large numbers, and by 1860 about 40,000 Mormons had established themselves in the state. They continued to prosper, and today Mormons make up almost 70 percent of Utah's population.

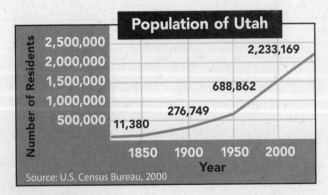

The passage above describes how the Mormon population has grown in Utah since 1847. As is stated in the last sentence, Mormons make up almost 70 percent of Utah's population.

The actual population of Utah is never revealed in the passage, so it is not possible to determine how many Mormons are living there. However, the graph shows how quickly the population of Utah has grown over the years and gives the population of Utah in specific years. Now it is possible to take 70 percent of the population number for the year 2000 to determine the approximate number of Mormons living there today. The information in the graph is important to better understand what was written in the passage.

Charts

A table is a kind of chart that uses rows and columns to provide data about a topic so the information can an easily be compared.

Read the paragraph below and then look at the table.

> When automobiles were first invented, they were costly to produce. Few people could afford them. Henry Ford of Detroit, Michigan, found a way to make cars less expensive. In 1908 Ford invented the Model T, a reliable and affordable car. Because he mass-produced Model T cars on assembly lines, he was able to sell them cheaply and many people were able to afford them.

The table shows how the price of the Model T Ford decreased from the years 1911 through 1915. This helps readers better understand just how affordable the Model T became in the years after Henry Ford introduced the car in 1908.

Price of a Model T Ford	
Year	Price
1911	$780
1912	$690
1913	$600
1914	$550
1915	$360

Time Lines

A time line is a visual way to show a sequence of events in a period of time. Events that happened during that time period are placed on the time line in the order in which they happened.

Read the passage below and then look at the time line.

As a boy in the early 1800s, Frederick Douglass was an enslaved African American. He believed that he had to read and write if he wanted to be free someday, so he made it his goal to get an education. But he faced a big challenge. It was against the law to teach enslaved people how to read. Young Frederick worked in a place where men built ships. The workers labeled each piece they made with a letter that stood for where the piece would go. By watching the men, Frederick learned to identify and write a few letters.

Whenever he met another boy who could write, Frederick would boast that he could write just as well. Frederick would write the few letters he knew and dare the other boy to do better. As the other boy wrote different letters, Frederick would pay careful attention. Over time, Frederick learned to write well. When he grew up, he fled, or escaped, from slavery. He used his powerful writing and speaking skills to fight for human rights. He became famous as an abolitionist, a person who fought to end slavery. Frederick first met President Lincoln in 1863. Lincoln valued Frederick's opinions and friendship. The Civil War ended in 1865. That year, the Thirteenth Amendment abolished slavery in the United States.

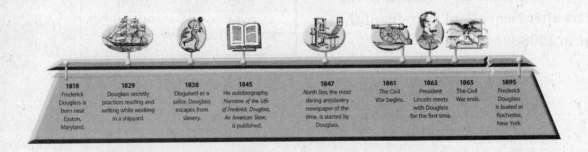

1818 Frederick Douglass is born near Easton, Maryland.

1829 Douglass secretly practices reading and writing while working in a shipyard.

1838 Disguised as a sailor, Douglass escapes from slavery.

1845 His autobiography, *Narrative of the Life of Frederick Douglass, An American Slave*, is published.

1847 *North Star*, the most daring antislavery newspaper of the time, is started by Douglass.

1861 The Civil War begins.

1863 President Lincoln meets with Douglass for the first time.

1865 The Civil War ends.

1895 Frederick Douglass is buried in Rochester, New York.

While the passage is written chronologically, it can be difficult to remember all the events that shaped Douglass's life. The time line is a good visual reminder of the major events in Douglass's life, and helps readers understand which events made him the important man he was.

Diagrams

A diagram is a drawing or series of drawings that explains an idea, a process, or how something works. It sometimes includes words as labels or descriptions. It may also include arrows or numbers to show the order in which things happen.

Read the passage below and then look at the diagram.

> Wind is an endlessly renewable resource we can harvest for energy. Right now, it is the fastest growing alternative energy source.
>
> Wind power causes little air pollution. However, some people dislike the way wind farms look. Others are concerned about the danger to birds and bats. The main problem with wind energy is the high cost of constructing wind farms.
>
> 1. Wind spins the blades, which turn the shaft.
> 2. The shaft turns a generator that makes electrical energy.
> 3. A transformer changes the electrical energy to usable electricity.
> 4. The electricity is delivered to buildings that are part of the nation's power grid.

Wind Power In Action

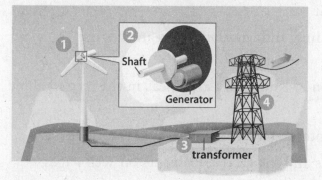

The text and diagram explain how wind power works. The diagram is a visual representation of the numbered steps in the text. Rather than describing the blades, shaft, and generator with words, the author has chosen to provide a diagram showing what each part looks like and how they are related. Readers can also better imagine what a wind farm might look like and understand the statement in the text, "some people dislike the way wind farms look." Without the diagram, the reader might not be able to visualize a wind farm.

Animations and Interactive Elements on Web Pages

You can learn information about a topic by reading words on a Web page. However, viewing animations, visuals, or interactive elements along with the text will increase your understanding of the topic and make learning more enjoyable. Often visuals, animations, or interactive elements will explain a process or show how something works.

Read the passage below and then view the animation titled Air Density.

Have you ever noticed that it is sometimes warmer on the second floor of a building than it is on the first floor? This is because warmer air rises more quickly than cooler air. When air is heated it becomes less dense and begins to rise. Density is a measure of how much mass is packed in a given space. The density of a substance determines if it will rise or sink. The air particles in the warmer air move faster as they become heated. When these particles spread out they become lighter and therefore rise.

Now follow these directions to view an animated video about air density.

1. Type in your *Common Core State Standards Literacy Handbook* into your browser's address bar.
2. Click on Part 2 Reading: Informational Text in the first Table of Contents.
3. Go to 2.3 Integration of Knowledge and Ideas in the second Table of Contents.
4. Click on Lesson A Interpret and Explain Visual Information.
5. Click on Animations and Interactive Elements on Web Pages.
6. Click on Air Density.

Density can be a difficult concept to understand—especially if you are only given a text as an explanation and not pictures. The animation of the hot air balloons does a good job of showing how the temperature of the air affects its density. The circles showing air particles inside and outside the balloon provide a clear visual representation of more or less density.

Turn to pages 137–145 to practice using visual information.

Name _____

Interpret and Explain Visual Information

Practice: Graph

Read the passage. Then look at the accompanying visual information and answer the questions.

> Earth and the moon are not the only objects revolving around the sun. Other planets do too. A planet is a large, round object that revolves around a star. A solar system is made up of a star and all the things that revolve around it. At the center of our solar system is the sun, a star. Eight planets, their moons, asteroids, dwarf planets, and comets revolve around the sun. The planets in our solar system are all different in size and distance from the sun. Some are made mostly of rock. Others are made mostly of gases. Each planet rotates as it revolves. The sun rotates too. Everything moves in space!

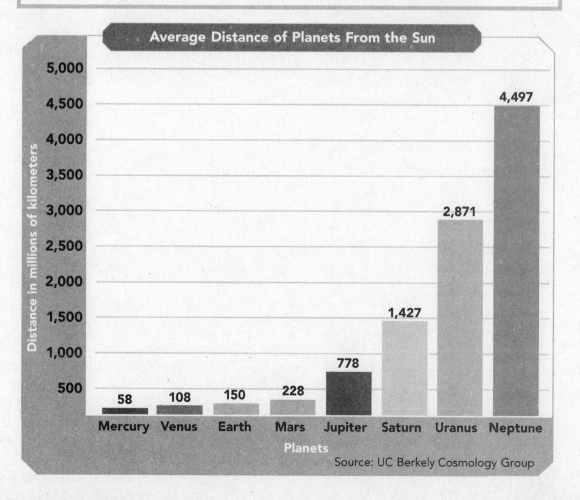

Average Distance of Planets From the Sun

Distance in millions of kilometers

Mercury 58, Venus 108, Earth 150, Mars 228, Jupiter 778, Saturn 1,427, Uranus 2,871, Neptune 4,497

Planets

Source: UC Berkely Cosmology Group

Name _____

1. How far is Earth from the sun?

_____

2. Which planet is closest to the sun?

_____

3. How does the graph help you better understand the passage?

_____

_____

_____

Name _____

Practice: Diagram

Read the passage. Then look at the accompanying visual information and answer the questions.

How to Make an Ant Farm

Materials: large jar, cardboard tube, soil, sand, ants, cloth, rubber band, and bits of food

Step 1: Place a cardboard tube inside a large jar. The tube makes the ants tunnel near the side of the jar so that you can see them.

Step 2: Fill the jar with soil and sand.

Step 3: Find an ant colony in your yard or a park. Catch at least 20 ants from the same colony to put in your farm.

Step 4: Try to find a queen ant. Queen ants are usually larger than the other ants. Some queen ants have wings.

Step 5: After you place the ants in the jar, cover the top with cloth. Use a rubber band to hold the cloth in place.

Step 6: Feed the ants once a week. Ants can eat tiny bits of food.

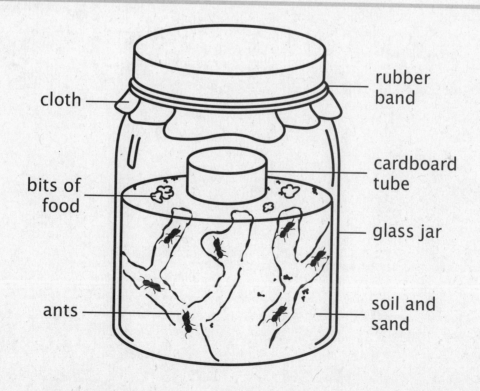

Name _____

1. What is the purpose of the cardboard tube in the jar?

_____

_____

2. What is the purpose of the cloth that is stretched over the opening of the jar?

_____

_____

3. How does the diagram help you better understand the instructions?

_____

_____

_____

Name _____

Practice: Chart

Read the passage. Then look at the accompanying visual information and answer the questions.

How much water is in the Great Lakes? The surface area of the Great Lakes is bigger than the states of New Jersey, New York, Connecticut, Rhode Island, Massachusetts, Vermont, and New Hampshire combined. Not only are the lakes wide, but they are deep too. If you spread them out, the lakes would submerge the United States under nine and a half feet of water. They contain about 20 percent of all the fresh water in the world. It is estimated that the lakes hold 95 percent of fresh surface water in North America. Scientists estimate that the Great Lakes contain six quadrillion gallons of water. (That's 6,000,000,000,000,000 gallons!)

The Great Lakes

	Surface Area (square miles)	Water Volume (cubic miles)	Maximum Depth (feet)	Number of People Who Use Water
Lake Superior	31,700	2,900	1,332	425,548
Lake Michigan	22,300	1,180	925	10,057,026
Lake Huron	23,000	850	750	1,502,687
Lake Erie	9,910	116	210	10,017,530
Lake Ontario	7,340	393	802	2,704,284

Source: EPA, 2006

Name _____

1. Which of the Great Lakes is the deepest?

_____

2. Which if the Great lakes has the most people using its water?

_____

3. How does the table help you better understand the passage?

_____

_____

_____

Name _____

Practice: Time Line

Read the passage. Then look at the accompanying visual information and answer the questions.

In May of 1932 Amelia Earhart became the first woman to fly solo across the Atlantic Ocean. It was a great accomplishment. She became even more well-known and made many more pioneering flights. From Hawaii to California, California to Mexico City, and Mexico City to New Jersey, Earhart forged ahead, setting records along the way. Only a few years later Earhart began talking about flying around the world.

After a lot of planning and a few setbacks, Earhart and her navigator, Fred Noonan, set off on their second attempt at flying around the world in 1937. Earhart and Noonan reported cloudy skies and trouble finding the island they were meant to land on. Then Navy ships did not hear anything more from Earhart's plane. Rescuers searched for weeks. There was no sign of Earhart or her plane. People have many different ideas about what happened to her. Her disappearance remains a mystery, even today.

Amelia Earhart disappeared almost 75 years ago. But her legacy remains with us. She proved to the world that women are equal to men. She taught people not to let anything stand between them and their dreams. Without Earhart's dedication, adventurousness, and free spirit, more girls today might still feel their choices are limited. Earhart lives in all our hearts every time we reach a little bit higher toward the sky.

Name _____

Important Events in Amelia Earhart's Life

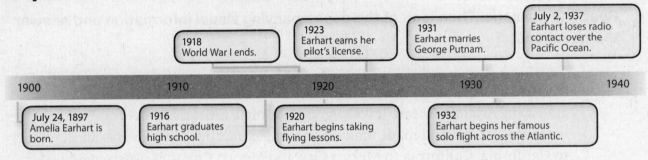

1. In what year did Earhart begin her famous solo flight across the Atlantic?

_____

_____

2. Did Earhart graduate high school before or after World War I ended?

_____

_____

3. How does the time line help you better understand the passage?

_____

_____

_____

Name _____

Practice: Animation

Read the passage. Then look at the accompanying visual information and answer the questions.

> Electricity is a form of energy. It involves the flow, or movement, of electric charges. The flow of charges through a circuit is called an electric current. In a circuit, electric current flows through metal wires. The electric circuits in many homes are parallel circuits. A parallel circuit has several paths. If one lightbulb in the circuit burns out, the others stay lit. Each lightbulb in a parallel circuit can be turned off and on individually with a switch.

- Type in your *Common Core State Standards Literacy eHandbook* address into your browser's address bar.
- Click on Part 2 Reading: Informational Text in the first Table of Contents.
- Go to 2.3 Integration of Knowledge and Ideas in the second Table of Contents.
- Click on Lesson A Interpret and Explain Visual Information.
- Click on Animations and Interactive Elements on Web Pages.
- Click on Practice.
- Click on Parallel Circuit.

1. What is the definition of a parallel circuit?

_____

_____

2. If one lightbulb in a parallel circuit is removed or burns out why does the other lightbulb stay lit?

_____

_____

3. How does the animation help you better understand the passage about electricity and parallel circuits?

_____

_____

Standard 8

Lesson B

Reasons and Evidence in Text

Authors of informational text make points, or state ideas about a topic. They then use **reasons** and **evidence** to support these points. Using reasons and evidence as support helps authors prove their points to readers.

Here's a model of how to identify and explain reasons ad evidence in text.

Reasons and Evidence in Text: Model

Read the passage below. Then see how the author uses reasons and evidence to support a point.

The Jewels of the Forest

by Sam Rockwood

Have you ever taken a jaunt through a scenic forest? What an amazing way to spend an afternoon! Imagine this: tall trees sway in the breeze. The cheerful music of melodic birds tickles your ears. Animals rustle through the brush. And if you're lucky, you spot a deer.

The forest is a constant flurry of activity, even when it appears peaceful and quiet. The sun, shining brightly on the plants, urges them to grow and flower. The rain, pouring down, soaks the soil, and thirsty roots reach for its moisture.

Deer amble through the forest, searching for food, their ears raised, listening for predators. Squirrels hurriedly dig for nuts while birds patiently construct their intricate nests, twig by twig.

The next time you stroll through the forest, take it all in. Breathe in the fresh air and sunshine, or feel the light rain on your face. Marvel at the way all the parts fit together, like jewels in a necklace, for all to enjoy.

How does the author use reasons and evidence to support a point in the passage?

In the first sentence of the second paragraph, the author makes the point that the forest is full of activity, even when it appears quiet and peaceful. Ask yourself: *What reasons and evidence does the author use to support this point?*

Now see the reasons and evidence underlined in the text.

The Jewels of the Forest
by Sam Rockwood

Have you ever taken a jaunt through a scenic forest? What an amazing way to spend an afternoon! Imagine this: tall trees sway in the breeze. The cheerful music of melodic birds tickles your ears. Animals rustle through the brush. And if you're lucky, you spot a deer.

The forest is a constant flurry of activity, even when it appears peaceful and quiet. The sun, shining brightly on the plants, urges them to grow and flower. The rain, pouring down, soaks the soil, and thirsty roots reach for its moisture. Deer amble through the forest, searching for food, their ears raised, listening for predators. Squirrels hurriedly dig for nuts while birds patiently construct their intricate nests, twig by twig.

The next time you stroll through the forest, take it all in. Breathe in the fresh air and sunshine, or feel the light rain on your face. Marvel at the way all the parts fit together, like jewels in a necklace, for all to enjoy.

The author mentions that the sun shines, the rain soaks the soil, deer look and listen, squirrels dig for nuts, and birds make nests. All of these details are examples of how the forest is full of activity, even when it appears quiet and peaceful.

Now turn to page 148 to practice explaining how an author uses reasons and evidence to support a point in another passage.

Name _____

Reasons and Evidence in Text

Practice

Read the passage below and answer the question that follows. Write your answer on the lines.

Bring on the City Life
by Paula Edward

Are you thinking of moving to the East Coast? Does the idea of living in a big city appeal to you? Do you like great seafood? If you answered yes to these questions, there is a Middle Atlantic state you should consider.

Although Maryland is one of the smallest states in terms of land area, it is rich in opportunities and options. In Baltimore, the biggest city in the state, residents enjoy hundreds of exciting activities. Baltimoreans can catch a thrilling baseball game at Camden Yards, enjoy delicious Maryland blue crabs at an inviting eatery in the Inner Harbor, or visit one of the universities in the city. They can even stop by the zoo.

Baltimore also offers other educational and cultural pursuits. The National Aquarium is located there, and the city has many respected art museums. The state capital, Annapolis, is less than an hour away. It is home to the United States Naval Academy.

Give Maryland and its cities a try. You'll find other places pale in comparison. Wait and see!

In the first sentence of the second paragraph, the author makes the point that although Maryland is small, it is rich in opportunities and options. How does the author use reasons and evidence to support this point?

_____

_____

_____

_____

Lesson C
Use Multiple Sources

Suppose your assignment is to write a report or give a speech on a certain topic.

1. First, you will need to do some research on your topic by going to the library or searching for reliable sources online.

2. Next you will need to take notes on what you learned from each source.

3. Then you will use what you learned from all the sources to write or speak knowledgably about your topic.

The following model shows how to use information from multiple sources in an assignment.

Use Multiple Sources: Model

Your assignment is to give a speech about the qualities of a hero. You decide to start finding out about famous heroes.

Suppose that you have found two different sources about heroic people in history. Read Source A below.

Source A

You may know people who like to talk about themselves. Marie Curie was not that kind of person. She went about her work quietly and cautiously. She didn't brag about what she did, although she could have. She was a woman of great wisdom. Marie Curie made discoveries that changed the world.

Marie Curie's work opened up a new field of medicine called radiology. Her experiments led to better ways of treating people with cancer and other diseases.

She was the first woman ever to win a Nobel Prize. This is a special prize given each year to people who do important work. Years later, Marie won a second Nobel Prize. She was the first person ever to do so.

Marie Curie lived at a time when few women were able to be scientists. She was born poor and was often ill. Yet she rose above all that to become a hero to the world.

What You Learn from Source A:

Source A is about Marie Curie. Even though she was born poor, was often ill, and was a scientist at a time when few women were, she was a hero to the world. She helped find better ways to treat cancer and other diseases. She was the first woman to win a Nobel Prize and the first person to win a second Nobel Prize.

Now read Source B.

Source B

> Although his father and grandfather had been enslaved, Benjamin Banneker was free. He wanted to use his hard-won freedom to make a difference in society, so he began studying. His studies led to a wooden clock, an almanac, and an important survey.
>
> First, Banneker envisioned a new clock. He disassembled a watch, sketching each gear inside. He formed gears from wood, using the sketches as a model. His wooden clock kept time for more than forty years!
>
> Banneker then looked for another way to benefit society. He studied astronomy and, consequently, wrote an almanac—a book containing statistical information.
>
> Along with science, Banneker studied math. He surveyed the Federal District, which is now the U.S. capital.
>
> He appeared to be ordinary, but Banneker was an inventor, scientist, and mathematician who made a difference.

What You Learn from Source B:

Source B is about Benjamin Banneker. He was a man whose father and grandfather had been enslaved. He wanted to make a difference, so he invented a new clock, wrote an almanac, and surveyed what became the U.S. capital. His work benefited society.

Connections between Source A and B:

Ask yourself: *What connections can I make between what I learned about Marie Curie and what I learned about Benjamin Banneker?*

- Both Curie and Banneker overcame obstacles.
- Both Curie and Banneker made a difference in society through their work.

What is the focus of your speech entitled "The Qualities of a Hero"?

After reading the information from multiple sources, you may decide that heroes are people who overcome obstacles in order to help society. This will be the focus of your speech. You will prepare your speech and use examples from your reading to support your main ideas.

Now turn to pages 152–156 to practice using information from multiple sources.

Name _____

Use Multiple Sources

Practice

Your assignment is to write a report about how to make changes for a better world. At the library, you have found two sources about how people in history successfully changed the world for the better. Read each source and tell what you learned from it. Then make connections between the sources in order to identify a focus for your report. Write your answers on the lines.

Source A

> At one time, African Americans in the United States did not have the same rights as white people. They had separate schools, and public places, such as restaurants, often had whites-only spaces. In the South Atlantic states, this segregation was common, but people worked together to change it.
>
> A turning point came one day in 1955, when an African American woman named Rosa Parks would not give up her bus seat to a white person in Montgomery, Alabama. She was arrested. Martin Luther King, Jr., encouraged all African Americans to stop riding the bus. A year later, the city of Montgomery decided to make segregated buses illegal.
>
> Dr. King asked African Americans to disobey the rules of segregation in nonviolent ways. In North Carolina in 1960, African American college students sat at a whites-only lunch counter. Angry people tried to make them leave but they stayed until it closed.
>
> In Albany, Georgia, African Americans tried to use the white waiting room of a bus station in 1961. Police ordered them to leave. Soon, African Americans across the nation were standing up for their rights.
>
> Because people worked together, things changed. On a warm day in 1963, at least 200,000 people joined together to march on Washington, D.C. Dr. King gave a powerful speech about his dream of all colors of people living freely together, and the government listened. Change happened slowly, but by the 1970s, legal segregation had disappeared.

Name _____

1. What You Learn from Source A:

_____

_____

_____

_____

_____

_____

_____

_____

Name _____

Source B

Imagine being a child and having to work hard in a factory every day. That's how it was in the early 1900s, before Lewis Hine and the National Child Labor Committee spread the message about the dangers of child labor. Even though laws against child labor existed in some states at that time, they weren't always enforced, and they weren't federal law. Besides, these laws did not protect children who had emigrated from other countries. These children often worked more than 72 hours a week (more than 10 hours every day!) and did not go to school. Sometimes the jobs they worked were dangerous, and many of them got sick or hurt. Then, in 1904, a group of people who were concerned about children working started the National Child Labor Committee. They hired photographer Lewis Hine to take and publish pictures of children working. Hine had studied sociology and worked as a teacher, so children were very important to him. To help people understand why child labor was wrong, he spent four years traveling around the country taking pictures of young children working. People saw his photos in pamphlets, such as "Child Labor in Gulf Coast Canneries." Eventually, Congress passed legislation to keep young children from working. Things might have been far different without Hine and the National Child Labor Committee.

Name _____

2. What You Learn from Source B:

_____

_____

_____

_____

_____

_____

_____

_____

_____

Name _____

3. Connections between Source A and Source B:

_____

_____

_____

_____

_____

4. What is the focus of your report entitled "How People Can Make Changes for the World"?

_____

_____

_____

_____

_____

Lesson A
Multisyllabic Words

Many words have two or more syllables. These longer words are called multisyllabic words, and there are several different strategies you could use to help you read them. In this lesson, you will learn more about how to read multisyllabic words.

Phonics

Phonics is the relationship that sounds have with letters. Phonics helps us know how words are spelled.

Many words rely on common sound-spellings. Knowing these common sound-spellings will help you connect the sounds with letters to read words.

Short Vowel Sounds

• Each vowel has a long and a short sound. The **short vowel sounds** are as follows:

/a/ as in *flattened*	/e/ as in *shelf*	/i/ as in *mill*
/o/ as in *blot*	/u/ as in *sum*	

• When a vowel comes between two consonants, it usually has a short sound.

Please pass me a hamburger bun.

Now turn to page 158 to practice identifying short vowel sounds.

Name _____

Short Vowel Sounds

Practice

A. Read the sentences below. Circle each word that has a short vowel sound between two consonants.

1. The police found the cash behind the shelf.

2. One thief ran to the dock.

3. One thief plotted to steal the bell.

4. The thieves hid behind a big tree.

5. They lay flat on the grass.

B. Circle the words with short vowel sounds. Then use three of them in sentences.

plate	leftovers	bleat	cove	loaded	mill
pas	neat	leave	crunches	plum	

6. _____

_____

7. _____

_____

8. _____

_____

Long a Spelled *ay, ai, a_e, ei, ea, a*

The long *a* sound can be spelled the following ways:

ay tod<u>ay</u>, str<u>ay</u>

ai r<u>ai</u>lway, dr<u>ai</u>n

a_e sl<u>a</u>t<u>e</u>, gr<u>a</u>z<u>e</u>

ei n<u>ei</u>ghborhood, sl<u>ei</u>gh

ea br<u>ea</u>k, gr<u>ea</u>tness

a b<u>a</u>by, l<u>a</u>dy

Now turn to page 160 to practice identifying long *a* spelled *ay, ai, a_e, ei, ea,* and *a*.

Name _____

Long a Spelled *ay, ai, a_e, ei, ea, a*

Practice

Read the following sentences. Write the words in the sentences that have a long *a* sound on the lines below.

1. The baby wood rats played outside today.

_____

2. Does it take long to make a crate for a snake?

_____

3. Rain in the desert can cause great flooding.

_____

4. The desert sunsets painted the sky bright colors.

_____

5. Did you see the snake that just slithered across the trail?

_____

6. Don't break away from the trail when walking in the desert.

_____

7. We heard the stray horses neigh as they grazed on desert bushes.

_____

8. We hiked in the desert until my legs ached and I felt faint.

_____

Common Core State Standards Literacy Handbook

Long *e* Spelled *ea, ee, ie, e*

The letters *ea, ee, ie,* and *e* often represent the long *e* sound, as in m**ea**n, m**ee**ting, th**ie**f, and m**e**.

Now turn to page 162 to practice identifying long *e* spelled *ea, ee, ie,* and *e*.

Name _____

Long *e* Spelled *ea, ee, ie, e*

Practice

A. Use the following words to complete the riddles.

leave	beef	please	be	piece	peeling	cheese

1. What do you call a cow on the ground?

   ground _____

2. What do you call a fly with one wing and two noses?

   I don't know, but when you find out, _____ let me know.

3. Why did the boy eat his homework?

   His teacher told him it was a _____ of cake.

4. Where do you _____ your dog while you shop?

   at a barking lot

5. Why did the banana go to the doctor?

   He wasn't _____ well.

6. What kind of mouse does not eat _____?

   a computer mouse

B. Circle any other words you find in the riddles with the spellings *ee, ea, ie,* and *e.*

Common Core State Standards Literacy Handbook

Long *i* Spelled *ie, i_e, igh, i, y*

The common spellings for the long *i* sound are *e, i_e, igh, i,* and *y.*

tie	bite	nighttime	mind	fly

Now turn to page 164 to to practice identifying long *i* spelled *ie, i_e, igh, i,* and *y.*

Name _____

Long *i* Spelled *ie, i_e, igh, i, y*

Practice

A. Complete the following sentences with one of these long *i* words.

kindness	drive	kite	wipe	pride
skylight	prime	sly	sighing	frightful
pies	spy	twice	find	

1. Jamal brought two _____ to the party.

2. Kate has a _____ in her bedroom?

3. Fernando went outside on a windy day to fly his _____.

4. The spaceship orbited the moon not once, but _____.

5. The astronauts wanted to _____ life on Mars.

6. It's more common to _____ a car than to pilot a spaceship.

B. Circle the word in each pair that has the long *i* sound.

7.   fitful   fighting

8.   dine   done

9.   fleas   flies

10. rip   ripe

11. trim   trying

12. high   hog

Long *o* Spelled *o_e, oa, ow, o*

The long *o* sound can be spelled several different ways.

| stol<u>e</u> (o_e) | f<u>oa</u>m (oa) | fl<u>ow</u>ing (ow) | m<u>o</u>ld (o) |

Now turn to page 166 to practice identifying long *o* spelled *o_e, oa, ow,* and *o*.

Name _____

Long *o* Spelled *o_e, oa, ow, o*

Practice

A. Fill in the blanks using each long o word in the box once.

boat	close	floating	shallow	know
most	don't	home	soaked	go
rowed	owned	Cole	foal	hoped

1. We were _____ in our _____.

2. Along the bank we saw the _____ beautiful white horse.

3. I asked _____ if he knew who _____ her.

4. He answered, "I _____."

5. Just then I caught sight of something small and brown and whispered,

   "She has a _____!"

6. "How _____ do you think we can get?" I asked.

7. I _____ to feed them the leftover apples from our lunch.

8. We _____ until the bottom scuffed against something below us, and

   I stepped out to wade through the _____ water to the shore.

9. To my surprise I promptly sank instead. I got _____!

   Cole thought it was hysterical!

10. "Let's _____ _____ I grumbled.

Common Core State Standards Literacy Handbook

Digraphs Spelled *ch, sh, th, wh, ph*

The letter pairs *ch, sh, th, wh,* and *ph* have one sound, even though there are two letters in the pair. Say the following words aloud and listen to the one sound made by the letter pairs.

ch chair, archway

sh shove, washer

th thirty, bother

wh whirl, anywhere

ph phrase, headphone

Now turn to page 168 to practice identifying digraphs spelled *ch, sh, th, wh,* and *ph*.

3

Name _____

Digraphs Spelled *ch, sh, th, wh, ph*

Practice

Use the clues to fill in the blanks with words that have *ch, sh, th, wh,* or *ph*.

1. I gave the money to my mother and _____.

2. I made a _____ before I blew out the candles on my birthday cake.

3. _____ is the library? Is it near Flower Street?

4. My camera helps me take good _____.

5. We stopped to rest on the park _____.

6. I'm going to the dentist because I have a cavity in one _____.

7. I picked up the _____ and called my friend.

8. Today I have crackers and _____ for a snack.

9. I put the plates, forks, and knives into the _____ and turned it on.

10. I made a bar _____ to show the daily sales at my lemonade stand.

Blends

In some **blends**, you hear the sounds of three consonants, as in *scrape* and *strain*. Sometimes, a blend is formed by a digraph and a third consonant, as in *shrug* and *thread*.

Now turn to page 170 to practice identifying blends.

Name _____

Blends

Practice

A. Circle the blend at the beginning of each word.

1. s p l e n d i d

2. s h r i n k i n g

3. t h r o n e

4. s t r e a m

5. s p l a s h e s

6. t h r e a d

7. s h r i m p

8. s c r u n c h

9. s p l i t t i n g

10. t h r o u g h

B. Read the sentence below. Then continue the story on the lines provided. Use at least six words with blends.

It was the first swim meet of the spring season. _____

_____

_____

_____

_____

_____

_____

Common Core State Standards Literacy Handbook

r-Controlled Vowels Spelled *ar, or*

Sometimes when the letter *r* comes after a vowel, the sound of the short vowel changes. Say the following words aloud and notice the sound of the vowels.

bat	bar	cat	cart	fox	for

Now turn to page 172 to practice identifying *r*-controlled vowels spelled *ar* and *or*.

Name _____

r-Controlled Vowels Spelled *ar, or*

Practice

Circle the word with the *r*-controlled vowels *ar* or *or* to complete each sentence. Then write the word on the blank to complete each sentence.

1. Please _____ me a salad and a glass of iced tea.

    far   order   port

2. The _____ used watercolors to finish his painting.

    form   barn   artist

3. The _____ on the rosebush are sharp.

    horns   thorns   stars

4. Did that _____ arrive in the mail for me.

    tarnish   core   parcel

5. We are going to have a birthday _____.

    party   cart   fort

6. My new _____ is nice and warm.

    scarf   tarp   farm

Common Core State Standards Literacy Handbook

r-Controlled Vowels Spelled *er, ir, ur*

The *r*-controlled sound you hear in *first* can be spelled *er, ir,* and *ur* in other words. The sound is found in the words *serpent, bird,* and *turkey*.

Now turn to page 174 to practice identifying *r*-controlled vowels spelled *er, ir,* and *ur*.

Name _____

r-Controlled Vowels Spelled *er, ir, ur*

Practice

A. Underline the vowel + *r* combination that represents the *r*-controlled sound heard first in each of these words.

1. b u r d e n

2. w h i r l w i n d

3. s t e r n l y

4. b u r r o w

5. s e r p e n t

6. p u r p o s e

7. b i r t h

8. p e r s o n

9. t u r n i p

10. g i r l f r i e n d

B. Now read the paragraph below. Find and circle six words that have the *r*-controlled sound heard first. Then continue the story. Use at least two words that have the *r*-controlled sound first, and circle the words with that sound. Remember that this sound can be spelled *er*, *ir*, or *ur*.

    One day, a raccoon climbed in the window of a house. He found a skirt on the floor. Holding it carefully in his mouth, he took it outside. Then he returned and carried away a small purse. Finally, he emerged with a purple shirt.

_____

_____

_____

_____

_____

    Common Core State Standards Literacy Handbook

Silent Letters

Say the words below aloud. In each word, the letter in bold is silent.

knives	plum**b**er	ri**d**ge	**w**riggle

Now turn to page 176 to practice identifying silent letters.

Name _____

Silent Letters

Practice

A. Quietly read the sentences aloud to yourself. Then circle the letter in the underlined word that you did not pronounce.

1. Rosa Parks <u>knew</u> that staying in her seat was the right thing to do.

2. We tried to push the rock out of the way, but it would not <u>budge</u>.

3. Christine <u>kneeled</u> down on the floor to pick up the paper she had dropped.

4. Martin's father needed a <u>wrench</u> to fix the piano bench.

5. The <u>tombs</u> in the cemetery remind us of those who came before us.

B. Using a dictionary, find at least five other words that begin with *kn* and *wr*. Write these words on the lines below and circle the silent letter in each one.

kn words   *wr* words

_____   _____

_____   _____

_____   _____

_____   _____

Soft *c* and *g*

When the letters *c* and *g* are followed by *e, i,* or *y,* they usually have a soft sounds /s/ and /j/. Say the following words aloud.

ceiling	*circus*	*cycle*
genius	*giant*	*gyroscope*

Now turn to page 178 to practice identifying soft *c* and *g.*

Name _____

Soft *c* and *g*

Practice

Circle the word with the soft *c* or *g* and write it on the line.

1. The people were _____ their plan would work.

   careful   certain   cornered

2. They wanted to work in the _____.

   city   country   crowd

3. We could exercise in the school's _____.

   gymnasium   grade school   group

4. The veterinarian provides _____ care to sick pets.

   glad   grateful   gentle

5. The veterinarian also makes sure the animals are free of _____.

   grease   gags   germs

6. Jamie likes to eat _____ for breakfast.

   cereal   corn   cupcakes

7. My mom took me to the pet store so we could buy a _____.

   game   goose   gerbil

8. Shelby has been learning to play the _____.

   clarinet   cymbals   castanets

Words with the Sounds /ü/, /u̇/, and /ū/

• These words have the /ü/ sound.

| spool, | grew, | move, | soup, | suit |

• These words have the /u̇/ sound.

| brooks, | should |

• These words have the /ū/ sound.

| cubes, | mule, | fuel |

• Notice the vowel spellings for the different sounds. Remember which sound they stand for in each word you learn.

Now turn to page 180 to practice identifying words with the sounds /ü/, /u̇/, and /ū/.

Name _____

Vowel Sounds /ü/, /ů/, and /ū/

Practice

A. Read each word. Circle the letters that make the sounds /ü/, /ů/, or /ū/.

1. w o u l d

2. d u n e

3. m u l e

4. k n e w

5. l o o k i n g

6. s c o o p

7. b o o k s

8. w o o d

9. u s e d

10. f o o d

B. Read the words below. Draw a line to match the words with the same vowel sound.

brook   soon

grew   could

mute   fuel

Diphthongs Spelled *oi*, *oy*, *ou*, *ow*

- The spellings *oi* and *oy* can have the same sound, as in f**oi**l and b**oy**.

- The spellings *ou* and *ow* can have the same sound, as in c**ou**ch and n**ow**.

- Keep in mind that not all words containing *oi* have the sound you hear in *foil*, and not all words spelled with *ou* and *ow* have the sound you hear in *couch*. Examples that don't have these sounds include *coincide*, *could*, and *mow*.

Now turn to page 182 to practice identifying diphthongs spelled *oi*, *oy*, *ou*, and *ow*.

Name _____

Diphthongs Spelled *oi, oy, ou, ow*

Practice

In each row of words below, there is one word that does not belong. If the word does not have the same sound as the others, draw an X over it.

1. joy   foil   employ   onion

2. coil   destroy   oil   going

3. mouth   doubt   through   how

4. broil   doing   spoil   noise

5. couch   dough   cloud   crowd

6. enjoy   soil   shooing   toys

7. now   enough   crown   proud

8. brow   cow   low   down

9. annoy   voices   boil   porpoise

10. thought   shower   loud   trout

Variant Vowel Spelled *au, aw, al, all*

- The underlined letters in the following words show you different ways to spell the sound you hear in *tall*: b<u>a</u>ld, t<u>a</u>lk, str<u>aw</u>, c<u>au</u>ght.

- Notice that in *bald* you pronounce the *l*, but that in *talk* you do not.

Now turn to page 184 to practice identifying variant vowel spelled *au, aw, al,* and *all*.

Name _____

Variant Vowel Spelled *au, aw, al, all*

Practice

Read the list of words below. Then sort the words into two columns. The left column is for words with the variant vowel spellings. The right column is for other words.

laws	catchs	malts	bows
sales	walls	bands	talking
wails	malls	strawberrys	taught

Words with the Variant Vowel   **Other Words**

_____   _____

_____   _____

_____   _____

_____   _____

_____   _____

_____   _____

Vowel Teams

Sometimes two or more letters together stand for one vowel sound. This is called a **vowel team**. When the vowels team up in a word, they stay in the same syllable.

oat/meal	rail/road

Now turn to page 186 to practice identifying vowel teams.

Name _____

Vowel Teams

Practice

Underline the vowel team in each word. Then write another word that has the same vowel team.

1. mailbox _____

2. seashore _____

3. mouthwash _____

4. steely _____

5. boastful _____

6. dreamlike _____

7. weighing _____

8. toaster _____

9. toil _____

10. sooner _____

-in, -on, -en

- Listen for the final schwa + *n* sounds at the end of the following words:

wood**en**	oft**en**	rais**in**	reas**on**	bac**on**

- These sounds can be spelled *-en*, *-in*, or *-on*.

Now turn to page 188 to practice identifying *-in*, *-on*, and *-en*.

Name _____

-in, -on, -en

Practice

Write a word from the box to complete each sentence. Underline the letters that represent the schwa + *n* sounds.

bacon	proven	button	eleven
cousin	dozen	women	reason
shaken	listen	common	cotton

1. The men and _____ helped collect canned goods.

2. Nine plus two is one less than a _____.

3. Do you know the _____ why the computer turned into a time machine?

4. Miners fried up lots of _____ for their breakfasts.

5. General stores in San Francisco sold yards of _____ for all the clothes the miners would need.

6. My great-grandfather had a _____ who was a gold miner.

7. The earthquake left them feeling very _____ up.

8. I love to _____ to stories about the Gold Rush.

9. Most of the miners could sew a patch or a _____ on their clothes.

10. The pigeon is a _____ bird in many cities.

Common Core State Standards Literacy Handbook

Syllable Patterns

Words with two or more syllables are multisyllabic words. One way to read longer words is to learn syllable patterns. Once you learn syllable patterns, you'll be able to read multisyllabic words more easily. In this section you will learn more about syllable patterns.

Closed Syllables

• A **closed syllable** is a syllable that ends with a consonant. The words *fan*, *am*, and *left* have closed syllables.

• Multisyllabic words have closed syllables too. For example, a two-syllable word with the **vowel-consonant-consonant-vowel pattern** may have one or two closed syllables. You can divide the word by syllables between the two consonants.

swallow—swal low	*hotdog—hot dog*
happen—hap pen	*problem—prob lem*

• A two-syllable word can also have the **vowel-consonant/vowel pattern**, or **VC/V**.

river—riv er	*cover—cov er*
robin—rob in	*planet—plan et*

Now turn to page 190 to practice identifying closed syllables.

Name _____

Closed Syllables

Practice

Draw a slash to divide each word below into syllables. Then write the syllables on the blanks provided.

1. c o p p e r _____

2. m e m b e r _____

3. p l a n n e r _____

4. m a r k e t _____

5. s u m m e r _____

6. s l e n d e r _____

7. f o s s i l _____

8. b l a n k e t _____

9. f i c t i o n _____

10. w i t n e s s _____

Open Syllables

• An **open syllable** ends with a long vowel sound. The words *be* and *me* have open syllables.

• Some multisyllabic words have an open syllable in the middle of the word. These words have the **vowel/consonant-vowel pattern**, or **V/CV**.

> *pilot—pi lot*   *bacon—ba con*

Now turn to page 192 to practice identifying open syllables.

Name _____

Open Syllables

Practice

Read the words below. Listen for the vowel sound in the first syllable and draw a slash to show where to divide each word. If you have doubts, look up the word in a dictionary.

1. human _____

2. secret _____

3. wiper _____

4. lazy _____

5. propel _____

6. meter _____

7. cider _____

8. silent _____

9. even _____

10. famous _____

r-Controlled Vowel Syllables

The **schwa-*r*** sound is a vowel sound often found in unaccented syllables. The three most common spellings for words that end in the schwa-*r* sound include *ar*, *er*, and *or*. For example, the schwa-*r* sound is what you hear at the end of **coll**ar, **dang**er, and **vict**or.

guitar	*mother*	*manor*

Now turn to page 194 to practice identifying *r*-controlled vowel syllables.

Name _____

r-Controlled Vowel Syllables

Practice

Use the words in the box to complete each sentence. Circle the letters that make the schwa-r sound in each word.

barber	zipper	anchor	harbor	popular	collar

1. Every time my clever _____ cuts my hair, he creates a work of art.

2. The Flemish oil paintings in the north tower are the most _____ exhibit in the museum.

3. My favorite collage is the one I made with the _____ from an old pair of trousers.

4. Aunt Susie finished her watercolor painting of the clipper ships in the _____.

5. I put a _____ and leash on my dog when we go for a walk in the park.

6. Uncle Tim thinks the old rusty tanker _____ in his front yard is beautiful!

Consonant + *le* Syllables

When a word ends in *-le*, those letters and the consonant before them form the last syllable. This is how you would divide the words into syllables.

set tle	gig gle	bub ble	tri fle

Now turn to page 196 to practice identifying consonant + *le* syllables.

Name _____

Consonant + *le* Syllables

Practice

Choose a word from the box to fill in each blank. Circle the letters that make the consonant + le syllable in each word.

bridle	little	adaptable	trouble
kettle	wiggle	Uncle	bottle

1. The wild horse would _____ from side to side and resist when

we tried to place a saddle on him.

2. _____ Cal, my father's brother, used to work on a farm that caught

and tamed wild horses.

3. After school, I watched a documentary about wild horses with

my _____ sister.

4. Wild horses are not the most _____ animals, which makes them

difficult to tame.

5. When working with horses, the trainer would often have _____

getting them to follow commands.

6. I poured a _____ of water into the _____

to make tea.

Common Core State Standards Literacy Handbook

Word Parts

Many multisyllabic words are made up of word parts. Some examples of word parts include prefixes, suffixes, and roots. When prefixes, suffixes, and roots are added to a word, they change the meaning of the word. In this section, you learn more about prefixes, suffixes, and roots.

To learn more about Word Parts, go to Lesson 6.3 Lesson C **Understand Word Parts** on Volume 2 page 262.

Prefixes

- When added to the beginning of a word, a prefix changes the meaning of the word.

- The prefixes *un-*, *non-*, and *dis-* mean "not" or "the opposite of."

dis + trust = distrust	to not trust
non + sense = nonsense	something that does not make sense
un + covered = uncovered	the opposite of covered

- The prefix *mis-* means "badly" or "incorrectly."

mis + spell = misspell	to spell incorrectly

- Each of these prefixes has a short vowel sound, and each adds another syllable to a word.

Now turn to page 198 to practice using prefixes.

Name _____

Prefixes

Practice

Underline the prefix in the following words. Then write the meaning of the word.

1. disobey _____

2. unsure _____

3. misbehave _____

4. nonsense _____

5. unhappy _____

6. dislike _____

7. misunderstand _____

8. disconnect _____

9. unbelievable _____

10. miscalculate _____

11. unusual _____

12. discontent _____

13. misread _____

14. unsettled _____

15. unafraid _____

Common Core State Standards Literacy Handbook

Suffixes

- **Suffixes** are word endings that change the meaning of a base word.

- The suffix -*ly* means "in a certain way."

> nicely = in a nice way

- The suffix -*less* means "without."

> breathless = without breath

- The suffix -*ness* means "the state of being."

> sickness = the state of being sick

- The suffix -*ful* means "full of."

> helpful = full of help

- The suffix -*y* means "characterized by."

> cheery = one who is characterized by cheer

- Sometimes when you add a suffix to the end of a base or root word, spelling changes are necessary.

> penny – y + i + less = penniless
> sun + n + y = sunny

Now turn to pages 200–201 to practice using suffixes.

Name _____

Suffixes 1

Practice

Circle the suffix in each word. Then circle the correct meaning of the word.

1. c l o u d y

    a. full of clouds   **b.** without clouds   **c.** in a clouded way

2. s u d d e n l y

    a. full of sudden   **b.** the opposite of sudden   **c.** in a sudden way

3. p o w e r f u l

    a. without power   **b.** the state of being powered by   **c.** full of power

4. s h o e l e s s

    a. full of shoes   **b.** without shoes   **c.** the state of having shoes

5. k i n d n e s s

    a. the state of being kind   **b.** full of kind   **c.** without any kind

6. l o u d l y

    a. without loud   **b.** full of loud   **c.** in a loud way

Name _____

Suffixes 2

Practice

Add the suffix to the end of each word. Remember to make any necessary spelling changes. Write the new word. Then use the word in a sentence.

1. happy + ly = _____

_____

2. thought + ful = _____

_____

3. care + less = _____

_____

4. kind + ness = _____

_____

5. fun + y = _____

_____

6. cheer + ful + ly = _____

_____

7. grace + ful + ness = _____

_____

8. hope + less + ly = _____

_____

Roots

- Words in English come from many sources. For example, the word *life* comes from the German word *leib*, meaning "body." Many words come from Latin or Greek. English words often have Latin or Greek roots. Knowing the meaning of common Latin and Greek roots can help you figure out the meaning of many words.

> **Latin Roots**
>
> *act* = do   *aud* = hear
> *mig* = move   *urb* = city

> **Greek Roots**
>
> *astro* = star   *bio* = life
> *tele* = far   *therm* = heat

- Words that have the **Latin root** *locat* have to do with places.

> locate

- Words that have the **Latin root** *duc* have to do with leading.

> educate

- Words with the **Greek root** *phon* have to do with sound.

> telephone

- Words with the **Greek root** *graph* have to do with writing.

> graphic

Now turn to pages 203–204 to practice using roots.

Name _____

Roots 1

Practice

A. Look at each word and identify the root. Circle the Latin roots and underline the Greek roots.

1. astronomer

2. immigrant

3. telephone

4. biologist

5. audience

6. action

B. Write the meaning of the word. Use a dictionary, if necessary.

7. thermostat

_____

_____

8. urban

_____

_____

Name _____

Roots 2

Practice

C. Complete each sentence with a word from the box that takes the place of the underlined words.

educate	relocate	location	conduct	deduce
graphic	telephone			

1. When people build in places where animals live, animals are sometimes forced to move to a new <u>place of activity or residence</u>. _____

2. Many zoos and parks <u>lead or guide</u> tours to help people learn about the animals that live there. _____

3. Many experts can <u>be led to a conclusion about</u> what kinds of animals live in an area just by looking at animal tracks. _____

4. Some parks and zoos <u>move to a different place</u> animals whose habitats have been destroyed. _____

5. It is a good idea to <u>lead</u> yourself <u>to learn</u> about the animals that live in your community. _____

6. Lee included a <u>diagram</u> in her report to illustrate one of the ideas she wrote about. _____

7. One way people communicate is by calling one another on a <u>device that transmits sound</u>. _____

Common Core State Standards Literacy Handbook

Lesson A
Develop Fluency

Reading with fluency means you're reading something the way it was meant to be read. In this lesson, you will learn about these fluency skills.

- Read with Purpose and Understanding
- Read with Accuracy
- Read with Appropriate Rate
- Read with Phrasing
- Read with Expression

Read with Purpose and Understanding

When you read with **purpose and understanding**, you read with the selection's intent in mind. For example, you would read an advertisement for a computer differently than a poem on friendship because each selection has a different purpose.

Read with Accuracy

When you read with **accuracy**, you read the words in a selection correctly. Self-monitoring strategies, such as sounding out an unknown word or using context clues to figure out an unknown word, will help you.

Read with Appropriate Phrasing

When you read with **appropriate phrasing**, you read the selection with pauses and stops. Identifying the groups of words that go together will help you know when to pause. Understanding the punctuation will also give clues about which words should be grouped together.

Read with Appropriate Rate

When you read with **appropriate rate**, you read the selection quickly, slowly, naturally, or with some combination of the three, depending on what the selection is about. You might read an advertisement for detergent quickly, a poem slowly, and a story at a natural pace.

Read with Expression

When you read with **expression**, you show the tone, or mood, of the selection. You might read a newspaper article about a tornado in a serious voice because it's a serious matter but a poem about friendship in a cheerful voice. In each situation, you change your voice to match the tone, or mood, of the piece.

Reading a selection fluently doesn't happen on the first try. It takes practice to get it right! It takes practice to understand the purpose of the selection, to understand all of the vocabulary, or to know how to read it.

Read with Purpose and Understanding

When you see a new selection, read it to yourself first. As you read, try to figure out what the selection is about. If you're not sure, ask yourself these questions:

- What is the topic?
- What is the selection about?

Understanding what the selection is about will help you understand its purpose. Authors write to entertain, inform, or persuade their readers. The purpose of the selection can influence how you speak when you read a selection out loud. For example, if the purpose of a selection is to persuade people to conserve water, you would want to show passion in your voice when you read the selection.

To help you identify the purpose, you can ask yourself these questions about the selection:

- Why did the author write this?
- How should the purpose influence the way I read it?

Now turn to page 207–208 to practice reading with purpose and understanding.

Name _____

Listen and Learn

Follow the steps below to listen to an audio version of the story. The story is also on page 208. Pay attention to the topic of the selection. Then answer the questions with a partner.

1. Type in your *Common Core State Standards Literacy eHandbook* addess in your browser's address bar.

2. Click on Part 3 Reading: Foundational Skills in the first Table of Contents.

3. Go to 3.2 Fluency in the second Table of Contents.

4. Click on Read with Purpose and Understanding at the bottom.

5. Click on Listen and Learn.

6. Click on the button.

Name _____

Kyle is a typical ten-year-old. He never imagined that he would have the important short-term goal of saving his younger brother's life.

Kyle was watching TV at his grandmother's house when his sister came running up to him. She was too scared to speak, but she pointed outside the window at the covered swimming pool.

When Kyle looked out he saw something move under the cover, and he jumped into action. He raced to the pool and pulled his baby brother from the water.

At a Cub Scout meeting, Kyle had learned how to breathe air into another person's lungs. He never imagined how scary it would be to use that skill, but he knew he had to overcome his fear to help his brother. Kyle met the challenge. He stayed calm, followed the steps he was taught, and saved his brother's life.

1. What is the topic of the text?

2. What do you think is the purpose of the text?

3. How does the purpose of the text influence the way the speaker uses her voice?

Common Core State Standards Literacy Handbook

Name _____

Fluency: Read with Purpose and Understanding

Choose one of the fluency passages. Read the passage silently to yourself. Then practice reading the passage aloud. When you are ready, read the passage aloud to a partner. Focus on reading with purpose and understanding by asking yourself following questions:

- What is the topic of the selection?
- What is the purpose of the selection?
- How will the topic and purpose influence the way I read?

Read with Accuracy, Appropriate Rate, Phrasing, and Expression

To be a fluent reader, you need to think about reading accurately, with appropriate rate and pacing, and with expression. This lesson explains these fluency skills:

- Accuracy
- Rate
- Phrasing
- Expression

Accuracy

Accuracy means reading the words in a selection correctly. There are strategies you can use to help you read words. For example, you can sound out the letters in a word or reread the sentence to figure out the meaning.

Rate

Rate is the speed with which you are speaking. Readers need to speak at an appropriate rate so listeners understand the message. Reading too fast or too slow makes the reading hard to understand. To sound natural, readers pause, stop, speak at a normal pace, speed up, or slow down at certain parts.

Phrasing

When you think about pausing, you are focusing on phrasing. When you pause or stop, you are chunking the text into small, meaningful phrases. All selections include vital clues that signal a stop or a pause. Commas and end punctuation indicate a pause or a stop. Other pauses come after words that are grouped together. Let's try it!

Read the following sentence:

When you were younger, you worked hard to learn many new things.

- The words *worked hard* should be read together. Try reading the sentence with a pause between *worked* and *hard*. Did you notice how the meaning of the sentence becomes unclear when you add a pause between *worked* and *hard*?
- Reread the sentence again, this time pausing at the comma and stopping at the period.

3

Expression

As you read a selection, think about the mood, or feeling that you get from a selection. The topic and words that an author uses influence the mood. There are many different ways that a selection can make you feel. Now, learn more about **mood.**

Mood

- You may think a story is cheerful, tense, serious, relaxed, funny, sad, or inspiring.
- If an author is writing about all of the problems a person keeps having with her car, you might think the mood seems helpless. However if the main character finds a way to fix all of the problems, you might think the mood shows relief.

Understanding the mood of a selection can help you read aloud with expression. If you read every word in the same way, your reading would sound uninteresting. To show expression, you change your voice when pronouncing different words and phrases. Now learn more about **expression.**

Expression

- If you are reading a story about winning a science fair, you would want to show excitement in your voice.
- If you are singing a lullaby to a baby, you might sing it in a hushed tone.

Now turn to pages 213–214 to practice reading with accuracy, appropriate rate, phrasing, and expression.

Name _____

Listen and Learn

Follow the steps below to listen to an audio version of the story. The story is also on page 214. Pay attention to the speaker's rate, phrasing, and expression. Then answer the questions with a partner.

1. Type in your *Common Core State Standards Literacy eHandbook* address into your browser's address bar.

2. Click on Part 3 Reading: Foundational Skills in the first Table of Contents.

3. Go to 3.2 Fluency in the second Table of Contents.

4. Click on Read Accuracy, Appropriate Rate, Phrasing, and Expression at the bottom.

5. Click on Listen and Learn.

6. Click on the button.

> Kyle is a typical ten-year-old. He never imagined that he would have the important short-term goal of saving his younger brother's life.
>
> Kyle was watching TV at his grandmother's house when his sister came running up to him. She was too scared to speak, but she pointed outside the window at the covered swimming pool.
>
> When Kyle looked out he saw something move under the cover, and he jumped into action. He raced to the pool and pulled his baby brother from the water.
>
> At a Cub Scout meeting, Kyle had learned how to breathe air into another person's lungs. He never imagined how scary it would be to use that skill, but he knew he had to overcome his fear to help his brother. Kyle met the challenge. He stayed calm, followed the steps he was taught, and saved his brother's life.

Name _____

1. What is the mood of the text?

2. What did the speaker do to show expression?

3. How did the speaker change her rate?

4. Now listen to the text again and focus on the phrasing the speaker uses. Pay attention to the last sentence, "He stayed calm, followed the steps he was taught, and saved his brother's life." Where did the speaker pause?

Name _____

Fluency

Choose one of the fluency passages. Read the passage silently to yourself. Then practice reading the passage aloud. When you are ready, read the passage aloud to a partner. Focus on reading with accuracy, appropriate rate, phrasing, and expression. Ask yourself the following questions:

- Can I read all of the words?
- What is the mood of the selection?
- How can I show expression?
- When should I change my rate?
- When should I pause or stop?

After you and your partner have read the passage aloud, talk about the choices you made. Discuss any changes that you think you could make in your reading and then read the passage again.

Story
Capturing Pictures on page 218
Maple Sap Mystery on page 219

Poetry
After Wind and Rain on page 220
The New Colossus on page 221

Informational Text
Wild Horses on page 222
Bring on the City Life on page 223

Use Self-Monitoring Strategies

As you read, you may see an unfamiliar word. If you do not know the word, you can use the following strategies to help you figure it out.

- **Reread** the sentence. Ask yourself, "Does the word make sense in the sentence?"

- **Read on** to see if the author explains the word later.

- **Slow down** to see if you missed any important details that give you clues about the word.

- **Sound out** the word. Think about the sounds that the letters make.

Try it! Select one of the fluency passages on page 217 to practice reading with fluency.

Common Core State Standards Literacy Handbook

Name _____

Fluency

Choose one of the fluency passages. Read the passage silently to yourself. Then practice reading the passage aloud. When you are ready, read the passage aloud to a partner. Focus on using self-monitoring strategies. Remember to:

- Reread.
- Read on.
- Slow down.
- Sound out the word.

Story

Poetry

Informational Text

Name _____

Practice

Capturing Pictures

Carly held her breath as the broad-tailed hummingbird fluttered near the cluster of wildflowers. She stared into her camera, waiting. A fly landed on Carly's arm. She flicked it away with a finger. The bird flew near a flower. The flower wasn't red enough, though. Carly waited. The bird flew to another flower. This one was too small. Finally, the bird hesitated over the largest, reddest flower. Carly began to snap pictures. She was certain that these would be some of the best pictures she had ever taken.

Carly raced home and uploaded the pictures onto her computer. She couldn't wait to see the results.

But when the pictures came up on the screen, she was disappointed. Carly studied them, then opened her photo journal. She wrote: "Hummingbird pictures: The bird's wings are a blur, not enough detail on flower, bird isn't close enough to the flower in any shot. Why aren't these the way I thought they would be?"

Name _____

Practice

Maple Sap Mystery

Jonah Brannigan awoke at midnight with a feeling of uneasiness. He stumbled out of bed, quickly donned his favorite flannel shirt and worn-out jeans, and whistled for his dog, Meena. Sugaring season had just begun, and it dawned on Jonah that the tubing that brought all the sap from the maple trees to the sugarhouse might be in jeopardy. Sometimes animals wandered through the trees and got caught in the tubing, interrupting the sap flow.

As he and Meena loped out of the door, Jonah saw a flash of gray near the sugarhouse, then blackness. He turned on his flashlight and searched the ground, but the only footprints he could see were those of his cat, Noodle. Meena also saw nothing out of the ordinary, so she and Jonah raced back into the house, shivering and annoyed.

The next morning, Jonah found tiny bite marks in the tubing near the sugarhouse. Could it be? He wondered. He hid behind a group of trees and waited. Sure enough, moments later, Noodle slunk to the tubing, chomped it with his tiny fangs, and lapped at the sweet sap that oozed out. Jonah smiled. He had found the midnight marauder!

Name _____

Practice

After Wind and Rain

Then the rain fell for two days straight
While the wind blew water all around.
And when it finally settled down,
A new world emerged, looking drowned.
After they came, the wind and the rain,
The hurricane over, but the damage done.
And the animals that survived the storm
Knew their problems had just begun.
After they came, the wind and the rain,
The habitats of many disappeared.
Some animals died, and some ran away,
But those that survived persevered.
After they came, the wind and the rain,
The land and the sea strived to improve.
But everything had changed so much
That man found they had to move.
A hurricane is a dangerous storm,
Damaging everything in its way.
Its wind, its rain, affect every life form,
And the roles that each one plays.

Name _____

Practice

The New Colossus

by Emma Lazarus

Not like the brazen giant of Greek fame
With conquering limbs astride from land to land;
Here at our sea-washed, sunset gates shall stand
A mighty woman with a torch, whose flame
Is the imprisoned lightning, and her name
Mother of Exiles. From her beacon-hand
Glows world-wide welcome; her mild eyes command
The air-bridged harbor that twin cities frame.
"Keep, ancient lands, your storied pomp!" cries she
With silent lips. "Give me your tired, your poor,
Your huddled masses yearning to breathe free,
The wretched refuse of your teeming shore.
Send these, the homeless, tempest-tossed to me,
I lift my lamp beside the golden door!"

Lazarus, Emma. "The New Colossus." Catalogue of the Pedestal Fund art loan exhibition at the National Academy of Design. 1883.

Name _____

Practice

Wild Horses

By the 1800s, huge herds of wild horses were roaming the open range.

Picture this: You must catch a wild animal that can run as fast as a train. You must tame that wild animal by riding on its back. You must teach that animal to follow your every command. And you must trust that animal with your life.

That is exactly what cowboys did when they caught, tamed, and rode wild mustangs.

Capturing a wild mustang was a team effort. One cowboy could not do it alone. Cowboys rode together on tamed horses in order to catch the wild mustangs. The cowboys used their fastest and strongest horses to chase the wild mustangs.

When the wild mustangs were exhausted, the cowboys drove them into a fenced corral. The mustangs couldn't see the fence until it was too late. Tired and thirsty from the long chase and glistening with sweat, the mustangs could run no more.

Name _____

Practice

Bring on the City Life

Are you thinking of moving to the East Coast? Does the idea of living in a big city appeal to you? Do you like great seafood? If you answered yes to these questions, there is a Middle Atlantic state you should consider.

Although Maryland is one of the smallest states in terms of land area, it is rich in opportunities and options. In Baltimore, the biggest city in the state, residents enjoy hundreds of exciting activities. Baltimoreans can catch a thrilling baseball game at Camden Yards, enjoy delicious Maryland blue crabs at an inviting eater in the Inner Harbor, or visit one of the universities in the city. They can even stop by the zoo.

Baltimore also offers other educational and cultural pursuits. The National Aquarium is located there, and the city has many respected art museums. The state capital, Annapolis, is less than an hour away. It is home to the United States Naval Academy.

Give Maryland and its cities a try. You'll find other places pale in comparison. Wait and see!

Lesson A
Write Opinion Pieces

Writers often share their opinions through writing. Being able to express your point of view and support it with reasons is an important skill. In this lesson, you will learn how to write these opinion pieces:

● Essay

● Book review

Essay

Writers often share their opinions through essays. In an opinion essay, the writer tries to convince the reader to share his or her point of view by providing strong arguments. An opinion essay may try to change readers' points of view, or convince them to act a certain way or accept the writer's explanation of a problem.

THINK AND WRITE
Purpose Why would you want to write an opinion essay?
Write your ideas in your journal.

Learning from Writers

Read this example of an opinion essay. Pay attention to the reasons the writer provides. How has she used reasons to support her opinion?

Opinion Essay: Student Model

A Power-ful Sun!

A lot of our energy comes from fuels such as oil, coal, and gas. One day we'll run out of them, but what can we do? We should use energy from the sun.

When the sun heats air, it rises and cooler air rushes in to take its place. The sun's energy is now wind energy! It can turn windmills that, in turn, can produce electrical energy.

In addition to causing wind energy, the sun also warms water. This water rises and evaporates. Then it falls as rain or snow. Now the sun's energy fills rivers. We can use this water to run generators that produce electricity.

Solar panels on houses collect the sun's energy. It can warm a house and heat its water supply. Special cells collect the sun's energy and change it into solar energy.

The more we use the sun, the less we'll need other fuels, and the cleaner our air will be.

Practice

1. **Thinking Like a Reader** What opinion does the writer share?
2. **Thinking Like a Writer** How does the writer try to convince readers to share her opinion?

Features of Opinion Pieces

Opinion pieces give the opinion of the writer and encourage the audience to share the writer's opinion.

Good opinion pieces have these features.

Writer's Opinion

Good opinion pieces clearly state the writer's opinion on a topic. The writer's opinion in "A Power-ful Sun" is underlined below.

A lot of our energy comes from fuels such as oil, coal, and gas. One day we'll run out of them, but what can we do? <u>We should use energy from the sun.</u>

Convincing Reasons

Why do you have the opinion you do? It is important to support an opinion, or point of view, with convincing reasons. You can support your reasons with facts or details.

The writer says the sun's energy can warm a house and heat its water supply. This is one reason we should use energy from the sun. She supports this reason by sharing details that explain it. The details she provides are underlined.

> Solar panels on houses collect the sun's energy. It can warm a house and heat its water supply. Special cells collect the sun's energy and change it into solar energy.

Logical Order

Presenting ideas in a logical order makes your argument stronger. Often writers save their strongest points for last so that they end their pieces on a powerful note. Read the writer's final sentence.

> The more we use the sun, the less we'll need other fuels, and the cleaner our air will be.

Why is it a good way to end the piece?

Linking Words and Phrases

Writers link their opinions and reasons using words and phrases. Some linking words and phrases are *for instance*, *in order to*, and *in addition*. Linking words the writer uses are underlined below.

> When the sun heats air, it rises and cooler air rushes in to take its place. The sun's energy is now wind energy! It can turn windmills that, in turn, can produce electrical energy.
> In addition to causing wind energy, the sun also warms water. This water rises and evaporates. Then it falls as rain or snow. Now the sun's energy fills rivers. We can use this water to run generators that produce electricity.

Create an Opinon Web

1. Reread an opinion piece.

2. In a circle, write the author's opinion.

3. Draw "arms" from the circle. On each arm, write a reason the author presents to convince readers to support his or her opinion. Number the reasons to show the order in which the author gives them.

4. Write whether the author's reasons convinced you to support his or her opinion.

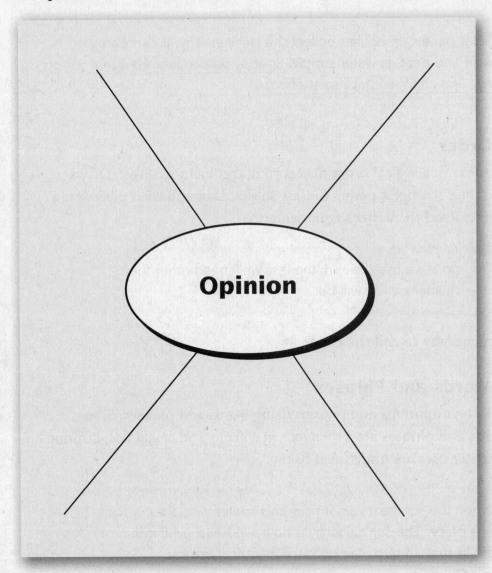

Writing Process

Now you are ready to write your own opinion essay. Follow the steps of the writing process to develop your writing.

- Prewrite
- Draft
- Revise
- Proofread/Edit
- Publish and Present

Prewrite

An opinion piece presents a writer's opinion, or point of view, about a topic and tries to convince an audience to agree with that opinion. Opinion writing may also influence an audience to take a certain plan of action.

Study the Model and Practice

As you're prewriting an opinion essay, it's important to consider the following.

Purpose and Audience

The purpose of an opinion piece is to persuade your reader to adopt your opinion, or point of view. You must use convincing reasons that will lead your audience to agree with your point of view.

> **THINK AND WRITE**
> **Audience** When planning an opinion essay, for example, you need to think about your reader. What is his or her opinion about your topic? What will you need to say to get your audience to think as you do? Use your journal to jot down your ideas.

Choose a Topic

Begin by **brainstorming** a list of issues or topics that you feel strongly about. Choose the issue most important to you.

Next, **explore ideas** by making a list of at least three reasons that support your opinion. For each reason, give facts and opinions to support it. Later, you will put your reasons in a logical order.

Why We Should Make Earth Day a Town Holiday

We need to clean up the environment.

Our landfill is almost full.

The water supply isn't safe (we had a bacteria scare last year).

Cleaning up would make the town a better place to live.

Earth Day celebrations would be fun.

Organize: Reasons and Explanations

To plan your essay, you need to think of reasons and information that support your opinion, or point of view. Writers support and explain their reasons with **facts** and **details**.

Which ideas from her list did the writer leave out?

Reason-and-Explanation Chart
My Topic: Earth Day should be a town holiday.
Reason: Our town doesn't do enough to help the environment.
Explanation: Our landfill is almost full. The water isn't safe and we had a bacteria scare.
Reason: We could do amazing things if we worked together.
Explanation: Midville's citizens cleaned the whole shoreline.
Conclusion: We should ask the mayor to make Earth Day a town holiday.

Turn to page 231 to make a reason-and-explanation chart for your opinion essay.

Name _____

Reason-and-Explanation Chart

Practice

Use the graphic organizer to record reasons and explanations for your opinion essay.

Reason-and-Explanation Chart
My Topic:
Reason:
Explanation:
Reason:
Explanation:
Reason:
Explanation:
Conclusion:

Research

Writer's Resources

You may need to do research to support your opinion about the topic of your essay. First, make a list of questions that your audience might have about your topic. Then decide which resources you will need to answer your questions.

What Else Do I Need to Know?	Where Can I Find the Information?
Why is our landfill almost full? How much trash do we throw away?	Interview the waste management company.

Choose Reference Sources

It is important to think carefully about your topic when choosing reference sources. If you are writing about a local issue, you might want to ask your community leaders for information. If you need recent information to support facts and opinions, use the *Readers' Guide to Periodical Literature* to find current magazine or newspaper articles. The Internet can also help you find information to support your opinion or position.

Use Your Research

After completing your research, add any new facts to your reason-and-explanation chart. For example, the student writer found out that her town throws away 5,000 tons of trash each year.

CHECKLIST: PREWRITING

☐ Did you think about your purpose and audience?

☐ Did you chose a topic that is important to you?

☐ Did you formulate your opinion and brainstorm reasons and explanations?

☐ Did you organize your ideas?

☐ Did you find answers to questions your readers might ask?

Draft

Before you begin writing your opinion essay, review the chart you made. Think about writing a paragraph for each reason you listed. Include details, especially facts, that support each reason. Arrange your reasons in a logical order. Save your strongest reason for last.

Study the Model and Practice

As you're drafting an opinion piece, it's important to consider the following.

Introduce the Topic

Begin your draft with a strong opening, like the one underlined below. A strong beginning will clearly introduce your topic, the issue you are writing about, and share your opinion.

> <u>Nothing is more important than cleaning our environment. We can do a better job keeping our town clean if we make Earth Day a town holiday.</u>
>
> Our town needs an Earth Day holiday. We don't do enough for the environment. Our town sends 5,000 tuns of trash to the landfill every year. The landfill is nearly full. Last years bacteria scare showed that even our water is not safe. We need a day to remember that our actions affect the environment
>
> If townspeople spent one day working together, we could do really good things. The citizens of Midville—a town smaller than ours—cleaned the whole shoreline. Just imagine how much good we could do!
>
> We should write to the mayor and ask her to declare Earth Day a town holiday. Then we should work together to make our town the cleanest in the state!

4

Write Your Body Paragraphs

Use your prewriting chart to write paragraphs that give reasons for your opinion, such as the reasons underlined below. Be sure that the ideas in each paragraph are related and support your purpose. For example, you may choose to use a separate paragraph for each reason you brainstormed. You would then include facts and details that support each reason.

Nothing is more important than cleaning our environment. We can do a better job keeping our town clean if we make Earth Day a town holiday.

Our town needs an Earth Day holiday. We don't do enough for the environment. Our town sends 5,000 tuns of trash to the landfill every year. The landfill is nearly full. Last years bacteria scare showed that even our water is not safe. We need a day to remember that our actions affect the environment.

If townspeople spent one day working together, we could do really good things. The citizens of Midville—a town smaller than ours—cleaned the whole shoreline. Just imagine how much good we could do!

We should write to the mayor and ask her to declare Earth Day a town holiday. Then we should work together to make our town the cleanest in the state!

Provide a Concluding Statement

Finish your draft with a concluding, or ending, statement, such as the one underlined below. Tie your conclusion back to your opinion. The conclusion of an opinion essay often asks readers to take action. What do you want your readers to do or think when they finish reading your essay?

> Nothing is more important than cleaning our environment. We can do a better job keeping our town clean if we make Earth Day a town holiday.
>
> Our town needs an Earth Day holiday. We don't do enough for the environment. Our town sends 5,000 tuns of trash to the landfill every year. The landfill is nearly full. Last years bacteria scare showed that even our water is not safe. We need a day to remember that our actions affect the environment
>
> If townspeople spent one day working together, we could do really good things. The citizens of Midville—a town smaller than ours—cleaned the whole shoreline. Just imagine how much good we could do!
>
> We should write to the mayor and ask her to declare Earth Day a town holiday. Then we should work together to make our town the cleanest in the state!

4

TECHNOLOGY TIP!

Be sure that your reasons are written in a logical order with the strongest one last. If not, use the cut-and-paste features on your computer to rearrange sentences or paragraphs in the order that will be most convincing to your audience.

CHECKLIST: DRAFTING

- [ ] Does your writing fit your purpose and audience?
- [ ] Did you introduce your topic and state your opinion?
- [ ] Did you include facts and details to support your reasons?
- [ ] Did you save your strongest argument for last?
- [ ] Did you end with a logical conclusion?

Revise

Now that you have completed your draft, it is time to revise it. Revising offers a chance to make sure your ideas are clear. Writers revise their writing before it is published to make sure their readers can understand the message. When you revise, reread your draft to add details, to delete unnecessary ideas or words, to substitute more precise language for overused words and phrases, or to rearrange ideas to make them clearer. Then have a partner review your draft and give you feedback.

> **TECHNOLOGY TIP!**
>
> It is easy to revise your work on a computer. Use the mouse to highlight information you want to rearrange. Next, hold down the button, "drag" the cursor to the spot where you want to move the information, and then let go of the button.

4

Study the Model and Practice

As you're revising, it's important to consider the following.

Elaborate

One way to improve your writing is to elaborate. When you elaborate, you add important facts, reasons, and details that might be missing from your writing. When you revise your opinion essay, you may need to include more reasons or details to prove your point. The facts and details that this writer added make her argument more convincing.

> Our town needs an Earth Day holiday. We don't do enough for the environment. Our town sends 5,000 tuns of trash to the landfill every year. The landfill is nearly full. We could use Earth Day to teach people about recycling.

The writer changed her wording to make her statement more forceful.

> If townspeople spent one day working together, we could do really good amazing things.

Use Transitions

Use words and phrases to link your opinion and reasons. Using transitions helps your writing flow and shows how your ideas are connected. This writer used the word *because* to link her opinion and reason.

> Our town needs an Earth Day holiday. ~~And~~ We don't because
>
> do enough for the environment.

TRANSITION WORDS

also
another
as a result
because
for example
for instance
in addition
in order to
therefore

4

Better Paragraphs

As you revise your writing, read your paragraphs to make sure each sentence relates to the purpose of the paragraph. Are there any other ideas you should add? Is there any extra information you should delete? You can make your writing clearer by taking out information that does not contribute to the purpose of your writing.

> If townspeople spent one day working together, we could do ~~really good~~ *amazing* things. The citizens of Midville—a town smaller than ours—cleaned the whole shoreline. Just imagine how much good we could do! ~~We have a better mall than Midville, though.~~

Peer Conferencing

Pair up with a partner and share your thoughts about each other's first draft.

As you read your partner's essay, use these prompts to guide your review.

☐ **Are the features of an opinion piece included in your partner's work?**

- states an opinion
- convincing reasons
- logical order
- strongest reason last
- uses transition words

☐ **Make sure to tell your partner what's good about the piece as well as what needs improvement.**

When you revise your opinion piece, you can use your partner's comments and suggestions to help you decide what changes need to be made.

TECHNOLOGY TIP!

Message boards allow others to comment on your writing. You can get feedback from classmates or your teacher by posting your writing on a class message board.

CHECKLIST: REVISING

- [ ] Does your writing fit your purpose and audience?
- [ ] Do you need to elaborate on your opinion or the reasons you included?
- [ ] Did you present ideas in a logical order?
- [ ] Did you use transition words to link one idea to the next?
- [ ] Do your sentences flow together?

Proofread/Edit

After you have revised your essay, you will need to proofread it to correct errors in grammar, mechanics and usage, and spelling. Use these proofreading marks to mark errors on your draft.

PROOFREADING MARKS

¶ new paragraph
∧ add
ℒ take out
≡ Make a capital letter.
/ Make a small letter.
ⓈⓅ Check the spelling.
⊙ Add a period.

Study the Model and Practice

Look at the proofreading corrections made on the draft shown below. What does the ^ symbol mean? When does the writer use that symbol?

> ## Make Earth Day a Town Holiday
>
> Nothing is more important than cleaning our environment. We can do a better job keeping our town clean if we make Earth Day a town holiday.
>
> Our town needs an Earth Day holiday. We ~~because~~ don't do enough for the environment. Our town sends 5,000 ~~tuns~~ tons of trash to the landfill every year. The landfill is nearly full. Last year's bacteria scare showed that even our water is not safe. We need a day to remember that our actions affect the environment.
>
> We could use Earth Day to teach people about recycling.
>
> If townspeople spent one day working together, we could do ~~really good~~ amazing things. The citizens of Midville—a town smaller than ours— cleaned the whole shoreline. Just imagine how much good we could do! ~~We have a better mall than Midville, though.~~
>
> We should write to the mayor and ask her to declare Earth Day a town holiday. Then we should work together to make our town the cleanest in the state!

Then follow these strategies to proofread your draft:

- **Reread your revised paper several times.** Check for different types of errors each time.

- **Check for punctuation errors.** Be sure you used commas and end punctuation correctly.

- **Check each sentence for correct capitalization.** Be sure to use capitals for street names, city names, and people's names.

- **Check for correct grammar and usage.**

- **Check for spelling mistakes.** Read your paper from the bottom to the top, word for word, to spot errors more easily.

TECHNOLOGY TIP!

Spell-checkers don't find homophones, words that sound the same but are spelled differently. Be sure to check carefully for the correct use of words such as *to, too,* and *two.*

CHECKLIST: PROOFREADING

☐ Did you spell all the words correctly?

☐ Did you use commas, end punctuation, and quotation marks correctly?

☐ Did you use capital letters where needed?

☐ Did you avoid grammar and usage errors?

Publish and Present

After revising and editing, you may choose to publish your writing to share with others. The writer used the Before You Publish checklist on page 244 to look her writing over one last time.

Practice

To publish your essay,

- give your revised draft one more careful look.
- make a neat final copy. If a computer is available, type your final draft.
- add illustrations, charts, or other visuals, if you wish.

After you publish, share your essay with others. You may wish to post it on a class Web site or read it aloud. Use this rubric to help evaluate your published piece.

Writing Rubric: Opinion Pieces

Score	Description
4 **Excellent**	<ul><li>presents a clear opinion with supporting details</li><li>presents reasons in a logical order</li><li>uses transition words to connect ideas</li><li>shows strong interest in the issue and connects to readers</li><li>uses a variety of sentences that flow smoothly</li><li>is free or almost free of errors</li></ul>
3 **Good**	<ul><li>presents a clear opinion with supporting details</li><li>presents reasons for an opinion in a logical order</li><li>uses some transition words to connect ideas</li><li>shows interest in the issue and connects to readers</li><li>uses a variety of complete sentences</li><li>has minor errors that do not confuse the reader</li></ul>
2 **Fair**	<ul><li>attempts to present an opinion, but supporting details are weak</li><li>presents reasons for the opinion, but not in a logical order</li><li>attempts to use at least one transition word to connect ideas</li><li>shows little connection with readers</li><li>is choppy and awkward</li><li>makes frequent errors that confuse the reader</li></ul>
1 **Unsatisfactory**	<ul><li>does not present an opinion</li><li>is poorly organized with disconnected ideas</li><li>does not use transition words to connect ideas</li><li>is dull and unconvincing</li><li>uses run-on sentences and sentence fragments</li><li>makes serious and repeated errors</li></ul>

TECHNOLOGY TIP!

Use available technology to share your writing.

- E-mail your published piece to your teacher or classmates.
- Display your writing on an electronic white board.
- Record it and save it as an audio file so others can listen to it on an mp3 player.

CHECKLIST: BEFORE YOU PUBLISH

- ☐ Did I keep my audience in mind?
- ☐ Did I achieve my purpose? Will my readers agree with my opinion?
- ☐ Did I include convincing reasons? Did I support them with details and facts?
- ☐ Did I present the information in a logical order?
- ☐ Did I write a strong opening sentence and a good closing sentence?
- ☐ Did I organize my paragraphs so that the ideas flow smoothly?
- ☐ Did I check for mistakes in grammar?
- ☐ Did I correct all errors in capitalization and punctuation?

Book Review

Writers write book reviews to share their opinions about books they have read. Book reviews help other readers decide which books they might want to read or not read. A book review provides a short summary of the book followed by the writer's reaction. The writer supports his or her opinion with solid, logical reasons.

THINK AND WRITE

Purpose Why would you want to write a book review? Write your ideas in your journal.

Learning from Writers

Read this example of a book review. Pay attention to the reasons the writer provides. How has he used reasons to support his opinion?

Sarah, Plain and Tall

Sarah, Plain and Tall, by Patricia MacLachlan, is a great story that takes place on a small farm on the Kansas prairie, far from any towns. In the story, Jacob advertises in the newspaper for a wife. He also wants her to be the mother for his children, Anna and Caleb. His first wife had died soon after Caleb was born.

Sarah answers his letter and comes from Maine for a visit. The two children really like her. However, she misses Maine very much, and they are afraid she will go back there. At the end of the story, Sarah decides whether to stay or return to Maine. You will have to read the story to find out what she decides.

I really like this story because the author shows how good and kind Sarah is. For instance, Sarah learns how to plow and how to ride a horse. She even gives the chickens names and will not eat them. Sarah tries to make herself part of the family. I think Sarah is kind and brave and would make a good mother.

I would recommend this book to anyone who likes stories with good characters or stories that take place long ago.

Practice

1. **Thinking Like a Reader** What opinion does the writer share about the book?

2. **Thinking Like a Writer** How does the writer support his opinion?

Features of Opinion Pieces

Opinion pieces give the opinion of the writer and encourage the audience to share the writer's opinion. A good opinion piece has these traits.

Writer's Opinion

The writer's opinion should be clearly stated, usually near the beginning. The writer's opinion about *Sarah, Plain and Tall* is underlined below.

> *Sarah, Plain and Tall*, by Patricia MacLachlan, is a great story that takes place on a small farm on the Kansas prairie, far from any towns.

Convincing Reasons

Why do you have the opinion you do? It is important to support an opinion with convincing reasons. Support your reasons with facts or details.

The writer's **reason** for enjoying the book is that the author shows how good and kind Sarah is. He supports this reason by sharing **details** from the text. The details he provides are underlined below.

> I really like this story because the author shows how good and kind Sarah is. For instance, Sarah learns how to plow and how to ride a horse. She even gives the chickens names and will not eat them. Sarah tries to make herself part of the family. I think Sarah is kind and brave and would make a good mother.

Logical Order

Presenting ideas in a logical order makes your argument stronger. Often writers save their strongest points for last so that they end their pieces on a powerful note. Read the writer's final sentence. Why is it a good way to end the piece?

> I really like this story because the author shows how good and kind Sarah is. For instance, Sarah learns how to plow and how to ride a horse. She even gives the chickens names and will not eat them. Sarah tries to make herself part of the family. I think Sarah is kind and brave and would make a good mother. I would recommend this book to anyone who likes stories with good characters or stories that take place long ago.

Linking Words and Phrases

Writers link their opinions and reasons using words and phrases. Some linking words and phrases are *for instance, in order to,* and *in addition.* The writer used linking words, underlined below.

> I really like this story because the author shows how good and kind Sarah is. For instance, Sarah learns how to plow and how to ride a horse. She even gives the chickens names and will not eat them. Sarah tries to make herself part of the family. I think Sarah is kind and brave and would make a good mother.

Create an Opinion Web

1. Reread a book review.

2. In a circle, write the author's opinion.

3. Draw "arms" from the circle. On each arm, write a reason the author presents to convince readers to support his or her opinion. Number the reasons to show the order in which the author gives them.

4. Write whether the author's reasons convinced you to support his or her opinion.

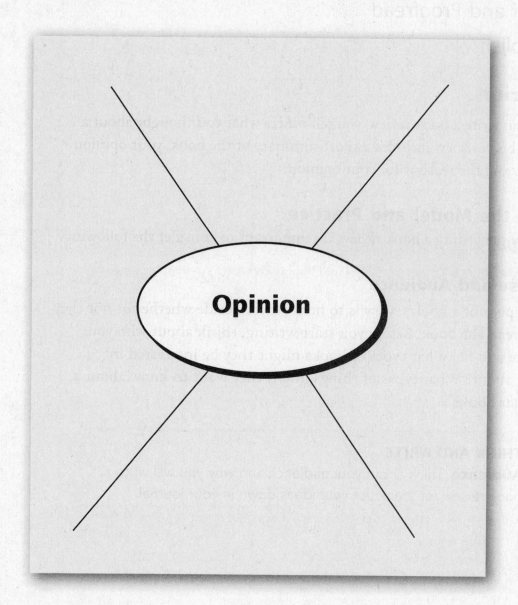

Writing Process

Now you are ready to write your own book review. Follow the steps of the writing process to develop your review.

- Prewrite
- Draft
- Revise
- Edit and Proofread
- Publish

Prewrite

When you write a book review, you tell others what you thought about a book. A book review includes a short summary of the book, your opinion about it, and the reasons for your opinion.

Study the Model and Practice

As you're prewriting a book review, it's important to consider the following.

Purpose and Audience

The purpose of a book review is to help others decide whether or not they should read the book. Before you start writing, think about who your audience will be. What types of books might they be interested in hearing about? What types of things might they want to know about a particular book?

> **THINK AND WRITE**
> **Audience** Think about your audience and why you will write a book review for them. Jot your ideas down in your journal.

Choose a Book

Begin by **brainstorming** a list of books you have read recently. Use the list to choose a book to review. Be sure to choose a book you feel strongly about.

After choosing a book, use your journal to do a freewrite about the book and your reactions and feeling about this book. Freewriting means writing without stopping in order to get ideas down on paper. It will help you generate reasons that explain why you did or did not enjoy the book.

Organize Your Ideas

There are two main parts to a book review: a summary and your opinion. You may use a graphic organizer to organize ideas for your book review.

Turn to page 254 to use a graphic organizer to organize your ideas for your book review. Page 255 shows how to fill it out.

Name _____

Book Review Organizer

Practice

Use the graphic organizer to organize ideas for your book review.

Title: Author:	
Summary	Opinion
Problem: Events: 1. 2. 3. Solution:	Reason: Details/Facts 1. 2. Reason: Details/Facts 1. 2.

Plan Your Summary Paragraph

To summarize a story, use the graphic organizer to write the **problem** and the important **events** in the story. Your audience may not have read the book, so be careful not to give away how the problem was solved.

To summarize a nonfiction book, use a graphic organizer to summarize the **main ideas** and the **details** that support the main ideas.

Be sure to include the title of the book and the name of the author.

Plan Your Opinion Paragraph

Use the graphic organizer to record your **opinion**. Then add one or two **reasons** why you feel the way you do. Add **details or facts** to support your reasons. For example, if you liked the book because the main character is a lot like you, give a few examples of things the character says or does that remind you of yourself.

Title: *Sarah, Plain and Tall*	
Author: Patricia MacLachlan	
Summary	**Opinion** I liked the book.
Problem: Jacob's wife died. He wants a new wife and a mother for his two children. **Events:** 1. Jacob advertises for a wife and a mother. 2. Sarah answers the ad and comes to visit. 3. The children like Sarah very much, but she misses Maine. **Solution:** Sarah decides.	**Reason:** The author makes Sarah a kind character. **Details/Facts:** 1. She learns to plow and ride a horse. 2. She named the chickens and wouldn't eat them. 3. She makes herself part of the family.

CHECKLIST: PREWRITING

☐ Have you thought about your purpose and audience?

☐ Have you chosen a book to review?

☐ Have you decided what to include in your summary?

☐ Have you formulated your opinion and brainstormed reasons why you feel that way?

Draft

Now that you have planned out your book review, you are ready to begin drafting. When you write a first draft, you get your ideas down on paper. Don't worry about making mistakes. You can fix them later when you revise and edit.

Study the Model and Practice

Keep the following in mind as you are drafting a book review.

Introduce the Topic

Begin your draft with a strong introduction, such as the one underlined below. A strong beginning will tell the name and author of the book you reviewed and clearly state your opinion about the book.

> _Sarah, Plain and Tall,_ by Patricia MacLachlan, is a great story that takes place on a small farm on the Kansas prairie, far from any towns. In the story, Jacob advertises in the newspaper for a wife. He also wants her to be the mother for his children, Anna and Caleb. His first wife had died soon after Caleb was born.
>
> Sarah answers his letter and comes from Maine for a visit. The two children really like her. However, she misses Maine very much, and they are afraid she will go back there. At the end of the story, Sarah decides whether to stay or return to Maine. You will have to read the story to find out what she decides.
>
> I really like this story because the author shows how good and kind Sarah is. For instance, Sarah learns how to plow and how to ride a horse. She even gives the chickens names and will not eat them. Sarah tries to make herself part of the family. I think Sarah is kind and brave and would make a good mother.
>
> I would recommend this book to anyone who likes stories with good characters or stories that take place long ago.

Write Your Body Paragraphs

Use your graphic organizer to write your summary paragraph. If you are writing about a story, be sure you don't give away the ending.

Next, begin your opinion paragraph. Writers often save their strongest reason for the end. What order will you use to present your reasons? Once you have decided, open your paragraph by stating your opinion. Then tell why you feel that way. Support your reasons with a detail or fact from the book. Examples of reasons are underlined here.

Sarah, Plain and Tall, by Patricia MacLachlan, is a great story that takes place on a small farm on the Kansas prairie, far from any towns. In the story, Jacob advertises in the newspaper for a wife. He also wants her to be the mother for his children, Anna and Caleb. His first wife had died soon after Caleb was born.

Sarah answers his letter and comes from Maine for a visit. The two children really like her. However, she misses Maine very much, and they are afraid she will go back there. At the end of the story, Sarah decides whether to stay or return to Maine. You will have to read the story to find out what she decides.

I really like this story because the author shows how good and kind Sarah is. For instance, Sarah learns how to plow and how to ride a horse. She even gives the chickens names and will not eat them. Sarah tries to make herself part of the family. I think Sarah is kind and brave and would make a good mother.

I would recommend this book to anyone who likes stories with good characters or stories that take place long ago.

Provide a Concluding Statement

Finish your draft with a concluding, or ending, statement. Tie your conclusion back to your opinion. In the conclusion of a book review, writers often tell who they think would enjoy the book.

Sarah, Plain and Tall, by Patricia MacLachlan, is a great story that takes place on a small farm on the Kansas prairie, far from any towns. In the story, Jacob advertises in the newspaper for a wife. He also wants her to be the mother for his children, Anna and Caleb. His first wife had died soon after Caleb was born.

Sarah answers his letter and comes from Maine for a visit. The two children really like her. However, she misses Maine very much, and they are afraid she will go back there. At the end of the story, Sarah decides whether to stay or return to Maine. You will have to read the story to find out what she decides.

I really like this story because the author shows how good and kind Sarah is. For instance, Sarah learns how to plow and how to ride a horse. She even gives the chickens names and will not eat them. Sarah tries to make herself part of the family. I think Sarah is kind and brave and would make a good mother.

<u>I would recommend this book to anyone who likes stories with good characters or stories that take place long ago.</u>

TECHNOLOGY TIP!

Use a word processor to type your draft. A word processor makes it easy to go back and add or delete ideas as you draft.

CHECKLIST: DRAFTING

- ☐ Does your writing fit your purpose and audience?
- ☐ Did you write a good topic sentence?
- ☐ Did you summarize the book without giving away the entire plot?
- ☐ Did you support your opinion with reasons?

Revise

Now that you have completed your draft, it is time to revise it. Revising offers a chance to make sure your ideas are clear. Writers revise their writing before it is published to make sure their readers can understand the message. When you revise, reread your draft to add details, to delete unnecessary ideas or words, to substitute stronger, more precise language for overused words and phrases, or to rearrange ideas to make them clearer. Then have a partner review your draft and give you feedback.

Study the Model and Practice

As you're revising your book review, it's important to consider the following.

Elaborate

One way to improve your writing is to elaborate. When you elaborate, you add important ideas and details that might be missing from your writing. When you revise your book review, you may need to add details to help you prove your point.

This writer added details to show what Sarah is like.

I really like this story because the author shows

how good and kind Sarah is. Sarah learns how

to plow. *and how to ride a horse*

Transitions

Use words and phrases to link your opinion and reasons. Using transitions helps your writing flow and shows how your ideas are connected.

I really like this story because the author shows
For instance,
how good and kind Sarah is. ^Sarah learns how to

plow and how to ride a horse.

Reread your draft. Add transitions to help readers understand how your ideas are connected.

TRANSITION WORDS

also
another
as a result
for example
for instance
in addition
in order to
therefore

Better Paragraphs

As you revise your writing, read your paragraphs to make sure each sentence relates to the purpose of the paragraph. Are there any other ideas you should add? Is there any extra information you should delete? You can make your writing clearer by taking out information that does not contribute to the purpose of your writing.

Sarah answers his letter and comes from Maine for a visit. ~~I haven't been to Maine before.~~ The two children really like her. However, she misses Maine very much, and they are afraid she will go back there. At the end of the story, Sarah decides whether to stay or return to Maine. You will have to read the story to find out what she decides.

Peer Conferencing

Take a break from writing. Give your partner a chance to read a copy of your first draft and to suggest changes that will make it better.

As you read your partner's draft, use these prompts to guide your review.

☐ **Are the features of an opinion piece included in your partner's work?**
- states an opinion
- convincing reasons
- logical order
- strongest reason last
- uses transition words

☐ **Make sure to tell your partner what's good about the piece as well as what needs improvement.**

When you revise your opinion piece, you can use your partner's comments and suggestions to help you decide what changes need to be made.

CHECKLIST: REVISING

☐ Does your writing fit your purpose and audience?

☐ Do you need to elaborate on your opinion or the reasons you included?

☐ Did you present ideas in a logical order?

☐ Did you use transition words to link one idea to the next?

☐ Do your sentences flow together?

Proofread/Edit

After you have revised your book review, you will need to proofread it to correct errors in grammar, mechanics and usage, and spelling. Use these proofreading marks to mark errors on your draft.

PROOFREADING MARKS

¶ new paragraph

∧ add

ℒ take out

≡ Make a capital letter.

╱ Make a small letter.

⑤℗ Check the spelling.

⊙ Add a period.

Study the Model and Practice

Look at the proofreading corrections made on the draft shown below. What does the / symbol mean? When does the writer use that symbol?

Sarah, Plain and Tall

Sarah, Plain and Tall, by Patricia MacLachlan, is a great story that takes place on a small farm on the Kansas Prairie far from any towns. In the story, Jacob ~~advertizes~~ SP advertises in the newspaper for a wife. He also wants her to be the mother for his children, Anna and Caleb. His first wife had did soon after Caleb was born.

Sarah answers his letter and comes from Maine for a visit. ~~I haven't been to Maine before.~~ The two children really like her. However, she misses Maine very much, and they are afraid she will go back there. At the end of the story, Sarah decides whether to stay or return to Maine. You ~~has~~ will have to read the story to find out what she decides.

I really like this story because the author shows how good and kind Sarah is. For instance, Sarah learns how to plow and how to ride a horse. She even gives the chickens names and will not eat them. Sarah tries to make herself part of the family. I think Sarah is kind and brave and would make a good mother.

I would recommend this book to anyone who likes stories with good characters or stories that take place long ago.

Common Core State Standards Literacy Handbook

Then follow these strategies to proofread your draft:

- **Reread your revised paper several times.** Check for different types of errors each time.

- **Check for punctuation errors.** Be sure you used commas and end punctuation correctly.

- **Check each sentence for correct capitalization.** Be sure to use capitals for street names, city names, and people's names.

- **Check for correct grammar and usage.** Be sure you have used complete sentences.

- **Check for spelling mistakes.** Read your paper from the bottom to the top, word for word, to spot errors more easily.

TECHNOLOGY TIP!
Spell-checkers don't find homophones, which are words that sound the same but are spelled differently. Be sure to check carefully for the correct use of words such as *to, too,* and *two.*

CHECKLIST: PROOFREADING
- [ ] Did you spell all the words correctly?
- [ ] Did you use commas, end punctuation, and quotation marks correctly?
- [ ] Did you use capital letters where needed?
- [ ] Did you avoid grammar and usage errors?

Publish

After revising and editing, you may choose to publish your writing to share with others.

The writer used the Before You Publish checklist to look his writing over one last time.

Practice

- Give your revised draft one more careful look.
- Make a neat final copy. If a computer is available, type your final draft.
- Add illustrations or insert a picture of the book cover.

After you publish, share your book review with others. You may wish to post it on a class Web site or read it aloud. Use this rubric to help evaluate your published piece.

Writing Rubric: Opinion Pieces

Score	Description
4 **Excellent**	<ul><li>presents a clear opinion with supporting details</li><li>presents reasons in a logical order</li><li>uses transition words to connect ideas</li><li>shows strong interest in the issue and connects to readers</li><li>uses a variety of sentences that flow smoothly</li><li>is free or almost free of errors</li></ul>
3 **Good**	<ul><li>presents a clear opinion with supporting details</li><li>presents reasons for an opinion in a logical order</li><li>uses some transition words to connect ideas</li><li>shows interest in the issue and connects to readers</li><li>uses a variety of complete sentences</li><li>has minor errors that do not confuse the reader</li></ul>
2 **Fair**	<ul><li>attempts to present an opinion, but supporting details are weak</li><li>presents reasons for the opinion, but not in a logical order</li><li>attempts to use at least one transition word to connect ideas</li><li>shows little connection with readers</li><li>is choppy and awkward</li><li>makes frequent errors that confuse the reader</li></ul>
1 **Unsatisfactory**	<ul><li>does not present an opinion</li><li>is poorly organized with disconnected ideas</li><li>does not use transition words to connect ideas</li><li>is dull and unconvincing</li><li>uses run-on sentences and sentence fragments</li><li>makes serious and repeated errors</li></ul>

TECHNOLOGY TIP!

To add a picture from a Web site, use the mouse to right click on the image. Click on *copy*. Then go to your word processing document. Click the mouse where you want to place the image. Right click again, and click on *paste*.

CHECKLIST: BEFORE YOU PUBLISH

☐ Did I keep my audience in mind?

☐ Did I achieve my purpose? Will my readers agree with my opinion?

☐ Did I include convincing reasons? Did I support them with details and facts?

☐ Did I present the information in a logical order?

☐ Did I write a strong opening sentence and a good closing sentence?

☐ Did I organize my paragraphs so that the ideas flow smoothly?

☐ Did I check for mistakes in grammar?

☐ Did I correct all errors in capitalization and punctuation?

More Ways to Review a Book

There are many ways you can present a book review. Here are a few ideas:

- Create a book jacket.
- Write a blog entry.
- Post it to a Web site that allows user reviews.
- Make a fact sheet listing 10 things you learned from the book.
- Write a news article as if the events of the book really happened.

Lesson B
Write Informative/Explanatory Texts

Explanatory writing presents information about a topic. It helps readers learn more about a topic or understand a process. In this lesson you will learn how to write these explanatory pieces.

- **Research Report**
- **How-To**

Research Report

When you create a report or an article that presents information or research about a topic, you are writing an explanatory piece. Explanatory writing presents information about a topic by using facts, details, descriptions, definitions, quotations, or examples to tell more about the topic.

THINK AND WRITE

Purpose Why would you want to write an explanatory piece? Write your ideas in your journal.

Learning from Writers

Read the explanatory writing example. Pay attention to the information the writer provides. How has she used details to develop the main idea of the piece?

Explanatory Writing: Student Model

Rain Forests

A surprising fact about plants and animals is that half of all species live in rain forests. However, only seven percent of rain forests remain in the world. If all the rain forests are destroyed, then half of all our species of plant and animal life will be, too.

Some of the animals living in rain forests are chimpanzees, toucans, frangipani caterpillars, butterflies, boa constrictors, tree frogs, and mountain gorillas. According to biologists, you can barely find two plants and animals that are alike because each is unique and beautiful in its own way.

Rain forests are our tropical treasures.

—Lisa Sharifi

Practice

1. **Thinking Like a Reader** What information does Lisa Sharifi give about rain forests?

2. **Thinking Like a Writer** How does Lisa show that many species live in rain forests? How do the content words *species* and *biologist* help to make the topic more specific?

Features of Explanatory Writing

Explanatory writing presents information about a topic. Good explanatory writing has these traits.

Main Idea

The main idea tells what the research report is about. Reread the opening paragraph of "Rain Forests." The main idea is underlined. Supporting facts and details in the passage explain how plants and animals make the rain forests a special place.

> A surprising fact about plants and animals is that half of all species live in rain forests. However, only seven percent of rain forests remain in the world. If all the rain forests are destroyed, then half of all our species of plant and animal life will be, too.

Important Information

Explanatory writing provides information. This information can include facts, definitions, details, quotations, and examples that support the main idea. This information can tell how, why, or when something happened.

> A surprising fact about plants and animals is that half of all species live in rain forests. However, only seven percent of rain forests remain in the world.

What information does the writer of "Rain Forests" give about rain forests?

Summarizes Information

Writers usually use several resources to research information about a topic. Then the author summarizes, or sums up, the information.

> According to biologists, you can barely find two plants and animals that are alike because each is unique and beautiful in its own way.

How do you think the writer got the information that is summarized here?

Concluding Statement

An author provides a concluding statement at the end of an explanatory piece to summarize the main idea and bring the piece to a logical close. Sometimes a conclusion makes a point as well as summarizes the main idea.

> Rain forests are our tropical treasures.

How does this concluding statement give readers a sense of closure?

Transition Words

Transition words and phrases help writers link ideas. Some transition words and phrases are *however, but, therefore, for example,* and *because.*

> A surprising fact about plants and animals is that half of all species live in rain forests. However, only seven percent of rain forests remain in the world.

What transition word does the author use?

Precise Language and Content Vocabulary

Writers use **precise**, or exact, language and **specific content vocabulary** when providing information about their topics.

Precise language helps readers understand the topic because it is specific, rather than general. For example, the student writer is careful to explain that this report is specifically about rain forests.

Specific content vocabulary, such as science words or social studies words, also helps explain your topic clearly. In the student model, the writer uses the science word **species** to explain what types of living things are found in rain forests.

> A surprising fact about plants and animals is that half of all species live in rain forests.

Common Core State Standards Literacy Handbook

Create a Features Chart

1. List the features of explanatory writing.

2. Reread a piece of explanatory writing.

3. Write one example of each feature in the writing.

4. What facts did you learn from the piece?

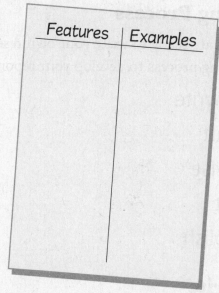

Features | Examples

Writing Process

Now you are ready to write your own research report. Follow the steps of the writing process to develop your report.

- ◯ Prewrite
- ◯ Draft
- ◯ Revise
- ◯ Edit
- ◯ Publish

Prewrite

Explanatory writing gives facts and information about a topic. You can use explanatory writing to share ideas about things you have learned through reading and research.

Study the Model and Practice

As you're prewriting an explanatory piece, it's important to consider the following.

Purpose and Audience

The purpose of explanatory writing is to explain or inform. In explanatory writing, you provide details that support your main idea. You use the information you have presented to draw conclusions about your topic.

Before you start writing, think about who your audience will be. Jot your ideas down in your journal. How can you organize your ideas so that your audience understands them? You also want your facts and information to be clear and complete.

> **THINK AND WRITE**
> **Audience** How does thinking about your audience help you decide what information to include in your writing? Jot your ideas down in your journal.

Choose a Topic

Begin by **brainstorming** a list of topics. Start with things you are interested in or topics that you want to learn more about. Use the list to choose a topic that interests you and will interest other people too.

After choosing a topic, **explore ideas** by listing information that you want to include in your writing.

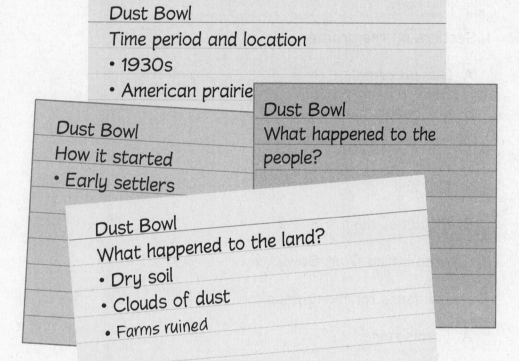

Dust Bowl

Time period and location
- 1930s
- American prairie

Dust Bowl

How it started
- Early settlers

Dust Bowl

What happened to the people?

Dust Bowl

What happened to the land?
- Dry soil
- Clouds of dust
- Farms ruined

Organize: Outlining

To help you organize your explanatory writing, you can use an outline to show the main topics you want to cover and the supporting information that should be included. How did the writer organize his notes in this outline?

Use your journal to create an outline for your research report.

OUTLINE

I. Settlers on the prairie

    A. Dug up grass

    B. Soil became loose

II. Drought in 1930s

    A. Dry soil

    B. Clouds of dust

    C. Area called Dust Bowl

III. Hard years for many people

    A. Farms ruined

    B. People left homes

Research

Writer's Resources

You will have to do research to get more information for your research report. Begin by making a list of questions. Then decide what resources you need to use to answer your questions.

What Else Do I Need to Know?	Where Can I Find the Information?
What area is called the Dust Bowl?	Look up the Dust Bowl in an encyclopedia.
Why did the soil become loose?	Call a history expert at a college or library.

Use an Encyclopedia

An encyclopedia is a useful source of information for a research report. When you use a CD-ROM encyclopedia, first type in keywords related to your topic. You will then see a list of articles about your subject. Click on the article that you want to read.

These are the keywords the writer typed in.

This is the best topic for finding the information needed.

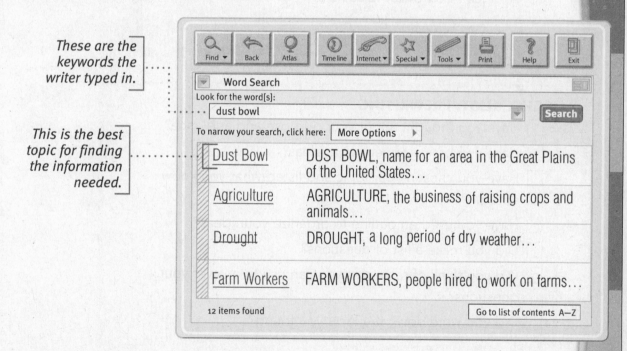

Consult Experts

Experts also have detailed knowledge about a subject. They can give you specific information that may be hard to find elsewhere. You can call, write, or e-mail an expert. Sometimes you will want to quote experts to support the main points of your report. Remember that experts are busy, so give them time to respond to your questions. Thank them for their help.

Use Your Research

In explanatory writing, you summarize information from a variety of sources, such as books and magazines. This writer got information from an encyclopedia and an expert. How was this information added to the outline?

I. Settlers on the prairie

   A. Dug up grass

   B. Soil became loose
      because the grass held the soil in place

II. Drought in 1930s

   A. Dry soil

   B. Clouds of dust

   C. Area called Dust Bowl *Colorado*

      New Mexico   Kansas   Texas   Oklahoma

CHECKLIST: PREWRITING

☐ Have you thought about your purpose and audience?

☐ Have you brainstormed topic ideas?

☐ Have you chosen your topic and listed what you know about it?

☐ Have you used an outline to organize your ideas?

☐ Did you make a list of questions?

☐ Did you think of resources you can use to answer your questions?

☐ Did you write down the facts you found?

Draft

Now that you have gathered your ideas for a research report, you are ready to begin drafting. When you write a first draft, you get your ideas down on paper. Don't worry about making mistakes. You can fix them later when you revise and edit.

Study the Model and Practice

As you're drafting an explanatory piece, it's important to consider the following.

Plan Your Paragraphs

Before you begin your explanatory writing, look at the outline you made. Think about organizing the information into paragraphs. Each paragraph has a main idea and supporting details such as facts, definitions, quotations, or examples.

OUTLINE

Each section of the outline can become one paragraph.

I. Settlers on the prairie

  A. Dug up grass

  B. Soil became loose
because the grass held the soil in place

II. Drought in 1930s

Main idea for second paragraph

  A. Dry soil

  B. Clouds of dust

  C. Area called Dust Bowl   Colorado
New Mexico   Kansas   Texas   Oklahoma

III. Hard years for many people

Main idea for third paragraph

  A. Farms ruined

  B. People left homes

Introduce the Topic

Once you have planned your paragraphs, consider how you will begin your draft. A strong beginning will clearly state your topic and capture your readers' attention.

Notice that the writer stated his topic at the end of the first paragraph, after giving the reader some background information about the topic.

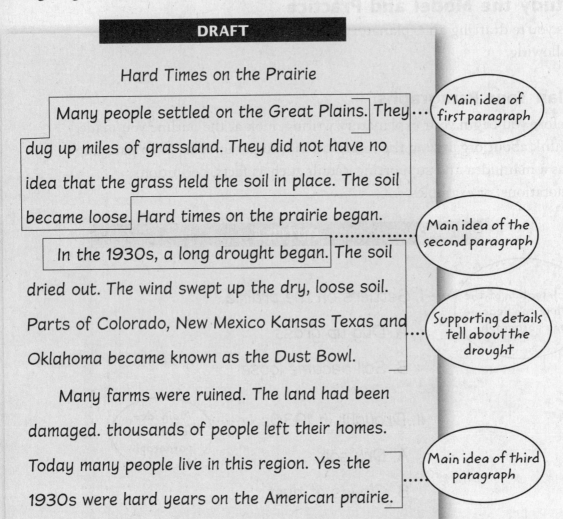

DRAFT

Hard Times on the Prairie

Many people settled on the Great Plains. They dug up miles of grassland. They did not have no idea that the grass held the soil in place. The soil became loose. Hard times on the prairie began.

Main idea of first paragraph

In the 1930s, a long drought began. The soil dried out. The wind swept up the dry, loose soil. Parts of Colorado, New Mexico Kansas Texas and Oklahoma became known as the Dust Bowl.

Main idea of the second paragraph

Supporting details tell about the drought

Many farms were ruined. The land had been damaged. thousands of people left their homes. Today many people live in this region. Yes the 1930s were hard years on the American prairie.

Main idea of third paragraph

Common Core State Standards Literacy Handbook

Provide a Concluding Statement or Paragraph

Finish your draft with a sentence or paragraph that gives your readers a sense of closure, or completeness. Use the ending to draw a conclusion or to restate your topic.

The writer ended his report by restating his topic.

DRAFT

Hard Times on the Prairie

Many people settled on the Great Plains. They dug up miles of grassland. They did not have no idea that the grass held the soil in place. The soil became loose. Hard times on the prairie began.

Main idea of first paragraph

In the 1930s, a long drought began. The soil dried out. The wind swept up the dry, loose soil. Parts of Colorado, New Mexico Kansas Texas and Oklahoma became known as the Dust Bowl.

Main idea of the second paragraph

Supporting details tell about the drought

Many farms were ruined. The land had been damaged. thousands of people left their homes. Today many people live in this region. Yes the 1930s were hard years on the American prairie.

Main idea of third paragraph

TECHNOLOGY TIP!

If you typed an outline on the computer, copy it to use as your draft. Make each item in the outline a complete sentence. Then add and rearrange details.

CHECKLIST: DRAFTING

- [ ] Does your writing fit your purpose and audience?
- [ ] Have you given important information about one main topic?
- [ ] Have you included facts, details, definitions, quotations, or examples to develop the topic?
- [ ] Have you included information from different sources?
- [ ] Does your writing follow your outline?

Revise

Now that you have completed your draft, it is time to revise it. Revising offers a chance to make sure your ideas are stated clearly. Writers revise their writing before it is published to make sure their readers can understand the message. When you revise, reread your draft to add details, to delete unnecessary ideas or words, to substitute more precise language for overused words and phrases, or to rearrange ideas to make them clearer. Then have a partner review your draft and give you feedback.

Study the Model and Practice

As you're revising an explanatory piece, it's important to consider the following.

Elaborate: Precise Language and Content Words

One way to improve your writing is to elaborate. When you elaborate, you use precise language and specific content words to add details and information that help explain the topic. When you revise your writing, you may wish to add words that state your ideas more precisely, or clearly. Look for opportunities to use science and social studies words to explain your topic.

The writer added a specific content word, *crops*, to elaborate on a point.

> and planted crops
> They dug up miles of grassland.

The writer used precise language to add details that help the reader understand his information.

> strong prairie
> The wind swept up the dry, loose soil.

Linking Words and Phrases

When you are writing, it is important to choose words that will help show the relationships between ideas. In explanatory writing, use transition words and phrases that make one idea flow into another. Linking, or transition, words signal for readers when ideas are similar, different, a result of something, or an exception.

> In the 1930's, a long drought began. The soil
> dried out.
>
> *Consequently,*

TRANSITION WORDS

and	also
another	thus
therefore	for example
as a result	before long
at the same time	however
when	because
but	consequently

Better Sentences

As you revise your writing, read your paragraphs aloud to see if the information is clear. Do the ideas in your paragraph flow easily from one sentence to the next? Combining sentences sometimes helps your ideas flow better.

Sometimes you can combine two short sentences to make one complex sentence that is more interesting.

> Many farms were ruined. The land had been
> damaged.
>
> *because*

Peer Conferencing

Take a break from writing. Give your partner a chance to read a copy of your first draft and to suggest changes that will make it better.

As you read your partner's report, use these prompts to guide your review.

> ☐ **Are the features of explanatory writing included in your partner's work?**
> - has a main idea
> - gives important information
> - summarizes information
> - provides a conclusion
> - uses transition words
>
> ☐ **Make sure to tell your partner what's good about the piece as well as what needs improvement.**

4

When you revise your explanatory writing, you can use your partner's comments and suggestions to help you decide what changes need to be made.

REVISE

Hard Times on the Prairie

In the early 1900s,
Many people settled on the Great Plains. They
and planted crops
dug up miles of grassland. They did not have no
As a result,
idea that the grass held the soil in place. The soil

became loose. Hard times on the prairie began.
Consequently,
In the 1930s, a long drought began. The soil
strong prairie   and made huge clouds of dust
dried out. The wind swept up the dry, loose soil.
Thus,
Parts of Colorado, New Mexico Kansas Texas and

Oklahoma became known as the Dust Bowl.
because
Many farms were ruined. The land had been
&
damaged. thousands of people left their homes.

Today many people live in this region. Yes the

1930s were hard years on the American prairie.

TECHNOLOGY TIP!

Many computers include a thesaurus. Learn how to use this feature to replace repeated words or change general words to more exact or vivid ones.

CHECKLIST: DRAFTING

- [ ] Does your explanatory writing fit your purpose and audience?
- [ ] Do you need to elaborate on any of the facts you have included?
- [ ] Did you present events in a logical order?
- [ ] Did you use transition words to link one idea to the next?
- [ ] Do your sentences flow together?

4

Proofread/Edit

After you have revised your explanatory writing, you will need to proofread it to correct errors in grammar, mechanics and usage, and spelling. Use these proofreading marks to mark errors on your draft.

Study the Model and Practice

Look at the proofreading corrections made on the draft shown below. What does the / symbol mean? When does the writer use that symbol?

PROOFREAD

Hard Times on the Prairie

In the early 1900s,
Many people settled on the Great Plains. They

and planted crops   any
dug up miles of grassland. They did not have no

                                    As a result,
idea that the grass held the soil in place. The soil

became loose Hard times on the prairie began.

                            Consequently,
    In the 1930s, a long drought began. The soil

strong prairie   and made huge clouds of dust
dried out. The wind swept up the dry, loose soil.

Thus,
Parts of Colorado, New Mexico Kansas Texas and

Oklahoma became known as the Dust Bowl.

                    because
    Many farms were ruined. The land had been

                                    their
damaged. thousands of people left there homes.

Today many people live in this region. Yes, the 1930s

were
where hard years on the American prairie.

Then follow these strategies to proofread your draft:

- **Reread your revised paper several times.** Check for different types of errors each time.

- **Check for punctuation errors.** Be sure you used commas and end punctuation correctly.

- **Check each sentence for correct capitalization.** Be sure to use capitals to begin a sentence and with street names, city names, and people's names.

- **Check for grammar and usage errors.** Be sure your sentences are complete.

- **Check for spelling mistakes.** Read your paper from the bottom to the top, word for word, to spot errors more easily.

TECHNOLOGY TIP!

Spell-checkers don't find homophones, which are words that sound the same but are spelled differently. Be sure to check carefully for the correct use of words such as *to, too,* and *two.*

CHECKLIST: PROOFREADING

☐ Did you spell all the words correctly?

☐ Did you use commas and end punctuation correctly?

☐ Did you use capital letters where needed?

☐ Did you avoid errors in grammar and usage?

Publish and Present

After revising and editing, you may choose to publish your writing to share with others. The writer used the Before You Publish checklist to look his writing over one last time. Read "Hard Times on the Prairie" and write about it in your journal. Do you think the piece was ready for publishing? Give reasons for your ideas. Then decide if you are ready to publish your draft.

Hard Times on the Prairie

by Daniel Harris

In the early 1900s, many people settled on the Great Plains. They dug up miles of grassland and planted crops. They did not have any idea that the grass held the soil in place. As a result, the soil became loose.

In the 1930s, a long drought began. Consequently, the soil dried out. The strong prairie wind swept up the dry, loose soil and made huge clouds of dust. Thus, parts of Colorado, New Mexico, Kansas, Texas, and Oklahoma became known as the Dust Bowl.

Many farms were ruined because the land had been damaged. Thousands of people left their homes. Yes, the 1930s were hard years on the American prairie.

Practice

- Give your revised draft one more careful look.

- Make a neat final copy. Type your report if a computer is available.

- Add maps, charts, photographs, or illustrations to your report.

After you publish, share your research report with others. You may wish to post it on a class Web site or read it aloud. Use this rubric to help evaluate your published piece.

Writing Rubric: Research Report

Score	Description
4 **Excellent**	• uses well-researched information to present a main idea • includes a strong introduction and conclusion • shows deep knowledge of topic and interests reader • uses transition words and accurate vocabulary • uses a variety of sentences that flow smoothly and guide reader • is free or almost free of errors
3 **Good**	• supports a main idea with solid research • has a logical flow of supporting facts and details • shows knowledge of the topic in a personal tone • uses relevant language and transition words • uses a variety of complete sentences • has minor errors that do not confuse the reader • presents limited research and has no main idea • has a weak introduction and conclusion • does not fully engage the topic and lacks a personal view
2 **Fair**	• chooses weak words for topic with few transition words • uses only simple or choppy sentences • makes frequent errors that confuse the reader • does not include research or provide facts about the topic • lacks a main idea or organizing structure • shows little understanding of topic and no personal style • relies on basic vocabulary with no transition words • uses run-on sentences and sentence fragments • makes serious and repeated errors
1 **Unsatisfactory**	• does not include research or provide facts about the topic • lacks a main idea or organizing structure • shows little understanding of topic and no personal style • relies on basic vocabulary with no transition words • uses run-on sentences and sentence fragments • makes serious and repeated errors

TECHNOLOGY TIP!

You may want to add graphics or multimedia to your document. Work with your teacher to use your computer to insert charts, graphs, clip art, or videos in your report.

CHECKLIST: BEFORE YOU PUBLISH

- [ ] Who was my audience? Will my writing be clear to them?
- [ ] What was my purpose for writing? Did I organize my information so that my audience can understand it?
- [ ] Did I add a title?
- [ ] Did I include explanations and facts that support my topic?
- [ ] Did I present the information in a logical order?
- [ ] Did I organize my paragraphs so that the ideas flow smoothly?
- [ ] Did I check for mistakes in grammar?
- [ ] Did I correct all errors in capitalization and punctuation?

How-to Writing

Have you ever read directions for making something? This is an example of how-to writing, a type of explanatory writing. How-to writing tells how to complete a particular task step by step.

> **THINK AND WRITE**
> **Purpose** Why would you want to write a how-to piece? Write your ideas in your journal.

Learning from Writers

Read this example of how-to writing. What process does the writer explain? What words does the writer use to tell you the order in which the steps were completed?

Explanatory Writing: Student Model

How Can Animals Help People?

Duffy is a dog who is part of a program called Pet Partners. Every week Duffy and other Pet Partners go to hospitals and other places. Their job is to help people who are very sick, sad, or lonely feel better. How did Duffy get to become a Pet Partner? It wasn't easy.

Step 1: Testing

First, Duffy needed to pass many different tests. Testers put food in front of Duffy. They bounced balls in front of him. They even brought in other dogs to distract him. In each case Duffy had to stay still until his trainer told him it was okay to move.

Step 2: Training

After Duffy passed all his tests, he needed to be trained. During his training Duffy learned how to help people. He learned to be patient with strangers. He learned how to be gentle with young children and very old people. After four months of training, Duffy was ready to be a Pet Partner.

Practice

1. **Thinking Like a Reader** What steps must a dog complete to become a Pet Partner?

2. **Thinking Like a Writer** Why does the writer tell about the tests first and Duffy's training second?

Features of How-to Writing

In how-to writing, the writer informs, or tells, the reader how to do something. The writer describes a process step by step. Good how-to writing has these traits.

Inform or Explain

Writers begin a how-to piece by clearly introducing the topic they will explain, which is often how to complete a certain task. What does "How Can Animals Help People?" explain?

> How did Duffy get to become a Pet Partner?

This question tells what the author will explain in the piece. The second and third paragraphs give related information telling how an animal becomes a Pet Partner.

Step-by-Step Directions

Step-by-step directions tell a reader how to complete a task and explain the order of the steps. This writer used headings to help readers identify the steps. The sentence below helps the reader understand what Duffy needed to do to become a Pet Partner.

The underlined part of the sentence shows what Duffy had to do first to become a Pet Partner?

> After Duffy passed all his tests, he needed to be trained.

Precise Language and Content Vocabulary

Precise, or exact, words help readers understand the process. For example, if you wrote about how to walk a dog, "Put the leash around the dog's neck" is more precise than "Put on the leash." This writer precisely describes the kinds of people Duffy learned to be gentle with.

> He learned how to be gentle with young children and very old people.

Specific content vocabulary, such as science words or social studies words, help explain your topic clearly. In the student model, content words, such as *trainer* and *test* explain how Duffy became a Pet Partner.

Facts, Definitions, Details, and Examples

Facts, definitions, details, and examples make an explanation easy to understand. The author of "How Can Animals Help People?" gives details and examples telling how Duffy was tested.

> Testers put food in front of Duffy. They bounced balls in front of him. They even brought in other dogs to distract him.

How do these details and examples help the reader understand the types of tests Duffy had to take?

Time-Order Words or Spatial Words

Time-order words, such as *next* and *last*, show the sequence of events. Spatial words, such as *behind* and *near*, tell where something is located. These words link ideas together and help make the steps in explanatory writing clear.

The author of "How Can Animals Help People?" uses this time-order word in the sentence.

> First, Duffy needed to pass many different tests.

Create a Features Chart

1. List the features of a good example of how-to writing.

2. Reread a piece of how-to writing.

3. Write one example of each feature in the writing.

4. Write why you think the how-to writing is easy to follow.

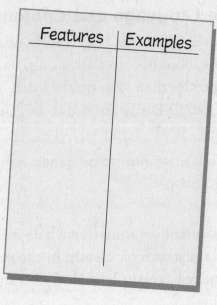

Features	Examples

Writing Process

Now you are ready to write your own how-to piece. Follow the steps of the writing process to develop your piece.

- ⬤ Prewrite
- ⬤ Draft
- ⬤ Revise
- ⬤ Edit
- ⬤ Publish and Present

Prewrite

In how-to writing, the writer informs, or tells, the reader how to do something. Writing an explanation can give you a way to tell others how to make something, complete a task, or find a particular place.

Study the Model and Practice

As you're prewriting a how-to piece, it's important to consider the following.

Purpose and Audience

The purpose of how-to writing is to explain something clearly to someone else. Instructions are presented in logical step-by-step order so that readers can easily understand them.

Before you begin writing an explanation, think about your audience. How can you be sure they will understand your explanation? Use words and examples that will be familiar to them.

> **THINK AND WRITE**
> **Audience** Write about how your audience will affect the way you explain directions.

Choose a Topic

Start by **brainstorming** different kinds of information that you could share with someone, such as instructions for making something or directions to a place.

After choosing your topic and audience, **explore ideas** by making a list of elements you will want to include in your explanation.

Directions to My Apartment

Look for apartment buildings
I live in Building D
North on Merrick Road
Right on Planet Road
Look for the school
Turn on the next street
Over the bridge
Four bridges in our town
Turn on June Lane

Organize: Sequence

How-to writing must clearly explain a process in a logical, step-by-step order. To plan your instructions, you can use a flow chart. Write a step in each box. How did the writer use her flow chart to organize the information from her list?

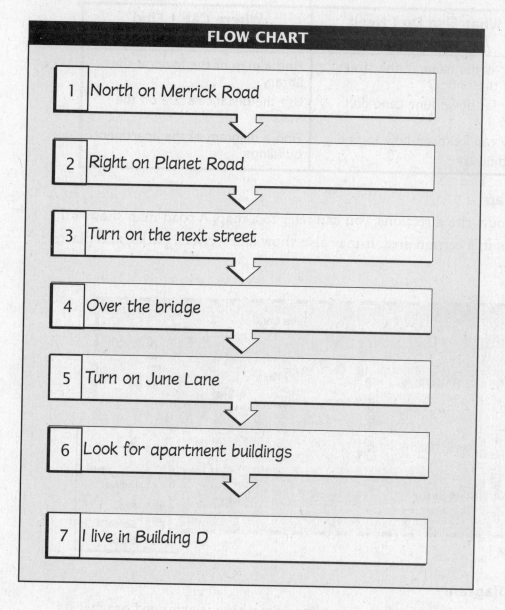

FLOW CHART

1 North on Merrick Road

2 Right on Planet Road

3 Turn on the next street

4 Over the bridge

5 Turn on June Lane

6 Look for apartment buildings

7 I live in Building D

4

Research

Writer's Resources

You may need to do some research to get additional information for how-to writing. Make a list of questions. Then decide what resources you need.

What Else Do I Need to Know?	Where Can I Find the Information?
What is the name of the street with the bridge?	Find a map of the town at the library.
How far down June Lane do I live?	Use the distance scale on the map.
How can I explain how to find Building D?	Find a diagram of the apartment buildings.

Use a Map

To help you write directions, you can refer to a map. A road map shows all the streets in a certain area. It may also show lakes, rivers, parks, and places of interest.

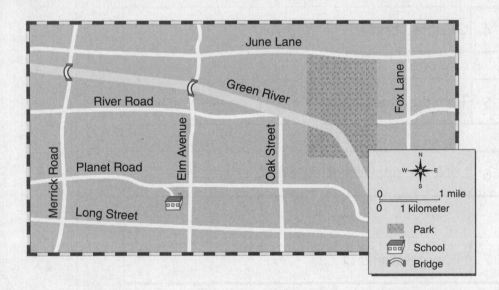

Use a Diagram

A diagram is a drawing that shows how something is arranged or what its parts are. A diagram can be a helpful resource for how-to writing. For example, if you were giving instructions for assembling a bicycle, a diagram might help you explain exactly how the pieces fit together.

Use Your Research

New information from your research can go into your flowchart. This writer found some important details to add to her directions. What did she add?

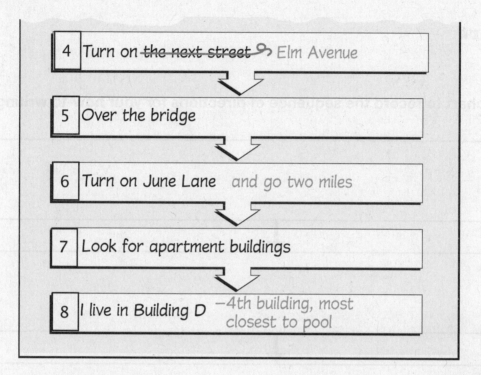

4 Turn on ~~the next street~~ Elm Avenue

5 Over the bridge

6 Turn on June Lane   and go two miles

7 Look for apartment buildings

8 I live in Building D   —4th building, most closest to pool

Turn to page 302 to use a flow chart to record the sequence of directions for your how-to writing.

Turn to page 302

CHECKLIST: PREWRITING

☐ Did you choose something to explain?

☐ Did you make a list of step-by-step instructions that are clear and easy to follow?

☐ Did you do any research to fill in missing details?

☐ Have you used a flow chart to organize your ideas?

Name _____

Flow Chart

Practice

Use the flow chart to record the sequence of directions for your how-to writing.

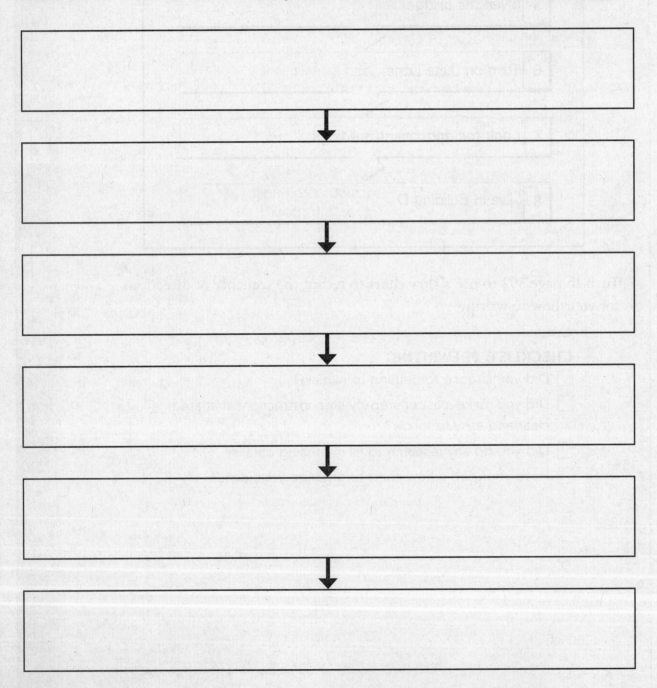

Draft

Now that you have gathered your ideas for a how-to piece, you are ready to begin drafting. When you write a first draft, you get your ideas down on paper. Don't worry about making mistakes. You can fix them later when you revise and edit.

Study the Model and Practice

As you're drafting an explanatory piece, it's important to consider the following.

Plan the Steps of Your How-to

Before you begin your explanatory writing, look at the flowchart you made. Think of dividing the information into paragraphs or numbered steps. Each paragraph or step has a main idea and supporting details such as facts, definitions, quotations, or examples.

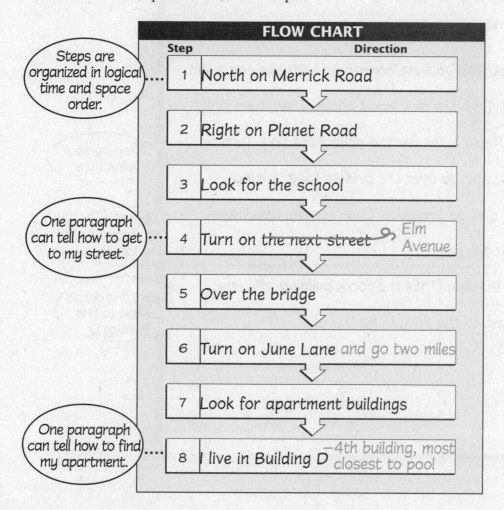

FLOW CHART

Step	Direction
1	North on Merrick Road
2	Right on Planet Road
3	Look for the school
4	Turn on the next street ⟶ Elm Avenue
5	Over the bridge
6	Turn on June Lane and go two miles
7	Look for apartment buildings
8	I live in Building D —4th building, most closest to pool

Steps are organized in logical time and space order.

One paragraph can tell how to get to my street.

One paragraph can tell how to find my apartment.

4

Introduce the Topic and Write the Steps

Once you have planned out your steps, consider how you will begin your draft. A strong beginning will clearly state your topic and capture your readers' attention.

Look at the ways this writer has used the steps in her chart to write a first draft of a letter. She grouped related sentences together in paragraphs. She presented the information in logical step-by-step order and added a short introduction.

DRAFT

129 June Lane

Sayville Maryland 21092

July 12 20__

dear Joanna

I'm so excited you are coming to visit! We can swim in the pool. Take Merrick Road north. Then, turn right on Planet Road. Look for the school building. Turn on Elm Avenue and go over the bridge. Next, turn on June Lane and go too miles. Look for the apartment buildings at the park.

I live in Building D. It's the forth building, the one most closest to the pool. I'll be there!

Your bestest

friend Mariana

Step-by-step directions

Main idea of second paragraph

Supporting details tell how to find Building D

Provide a Concluding Statement

Finish your draft with a sentence that gives your readers a sense of closure, or completeness. Use the ending to restate your topic or express a feeling.

In this friendly letter, the writer closed by telling her friend, "I'll be there!"

DRAFT

129 June Lane

Sayville Maryland 21092

July 12 20__

dear Joanna

I'm so excited you are coming to visit! We can swim in the pool. Take Merrick Road north. Then, turn right on Planet Road. Look for the school building. Turn on Elm Avenue and go over the bridge. Next, turn on June Lane and go too miles. Look for the apartment buildings at the park.

I live in Building D. It's the forth building, the one most closest to the pool. I'll be there!

Your bestest

friend Mariana

TECHNOLOGY TIP!

If you created a prewriting list or flowchart on your computer, you can copy it into a new document for writing your draft. Rearrange and add to the items or chart to create your draft.

CHECKLIST: DRAFTING

☐ Have you explained how to complete a process or a task?

☐ Are your steps in logical order?

☐ Have you given clear details that are easy to follow?

☐ Have you used time-order words (like *before* and *next*) or spatial words (like *left* and *right*) to help make your directions clearer?

Common Core State Standards Literacy Handbook

Revise

Now that you have completed your draft, it is time to revise it. Revising offers a chance to make sure your ideas are clear. Writers revise their writing before it is published to make sure their readers can understand the message. When you revise, reread your draft to add details, to delete unnecessary ideas or words, to substitute more precise language for overused words and phrases, or to rearrange ideas to make them clearer. Then have a partner review your draft and give you feedback.

Study the Model and Practice

As you're revising, it's important to consider the following.

Elaborate: Precise Language and Content Vocabulary

One way to improve your writing is to elaborate. When you elaborate, you add important steps or details that might be missing from your writing. When you revise your explanatory writing, you may need to add or take out details. Use precise, or exact, words that will make it easier for your readers to follow your instructions.

The writer added precise words that will help make it easier for the reader to follow directions. Notice the directional word *north*. This content vocabulary word also helps the reader follow the directions. Be sure to use content vocabulary in your how-to.

> to the traffic light
> Take Merrick Road north.
> ^

The writer added details to describe what the reader will see.

> red brick
> Look for the red brick apartment buildings at
> ^
> the park.

Time-Order Words, Spatial Words, and Transitions

When you are writing, it is important to choose just the right words for your topic and audience. Time-order words and spatial words show readers how ideas link together. Time-order words help readers understand what to do first, next, and last. Spatial words are helpful for giving directions to a place. These words tell where places are located in relation to one another. The writer added the words *right* and *across from* to help make the directions clearer.

> right
>
> Next, turn on June Lane and go too miles. Look
>
> red brick   across from
>
> for the apartment buildings at the park.

You may wish to use other types of transition words to connect your ideas, such as *another*, *for example*, *also*, and *because*.

SPATIAL WORDS

right	west	close to
left	north	behind
near	south	across from
far	next to	around
east	in front of	

Common Core State Standards Literacy Handbook

Better Sentences

As you revise your draft, check your paragraphs to make sure each one has a main idea. Do the facts, details, and examples in the paragraph support the main idea?

Sometimes writers make the mistake of including too much information in one paragraph. If a paragraph contains more than one main idea, you may be able to make your writing clearer by dividing it into two. Make sure each paragraph has a topic sentence.

> We'll have a great time.
> I am so excited you are coming to visit! We
> ⌗ Here are the directions to my apartment.
> can swim in the pool. Take Merrick Road north.

Peer Conferencing

Take a break from your writing and give a partner a copy of your original draft to read. Having someone else read your writing can be very helpful. Your partner may have suggestions and ideas that you haven't thought of.

As you read your partner's draft, use these prompts to guide your review.

☐ **Are the features of how-to writing included in your partner's work?**

- informs or explains
- step-by-step instructions
- clear details, facts, and examples
- time-order and spatial words

☐ **Make sure to tell your partner what's good about the piece as well as what needs improvement.**

When you revise your how-to writing, you can use your partner's comments and suggestions to help you decide what changes need to be made. Look at the changes this writer made after talking to a partner.

DRAFT

129 June Lane

Sayville Maryland 21092

July 12 20__

(Good step-by-step directions)

dear Joanna

I'm so excited you are coming to visit! We can swim in the pool. Take Merrick Road north. Then, turn right on Planet Road. Look for the school building. Turn on Elm Avenue and go over the bridge. Next, turn on June Lane and go too miles. Look for the apartment buildings at the park.

(Can you give more details about the school?)

I live in Building D. It's the forth building, the one most closest to the pool. I'll be there!

(Would a spatial word be helpful here?)

Your bestest

friend Mariana

129 June Lane

Sayville Maryland

21092

July 12 20__

dear Joanna

We'll have a great time.

I'm so excited you are coming to visit!

⌗ Here are the directions to my apartment. ^

We can swim in the pool. Take Merrick Road

to the traffic light

north. Then, turn right on Planet Road.

^   big white   on the right   left

Look for the ^ school building. Turn ^ on Elm

old wooden   ^

Avenue and go over the ^ bridge. Next, turn

right   red brick

^ on June Lane and go too miles. Look for the ^

across from

apartment buildings ^ the park.

on the left

I live in Building D. It's the forth building, the ^

one most closest to the pool. I'll be there!

Your bestest friend

Mariana

TECHNOLOGY TIP!

When you begin revising your draft, you can rename your document using the SAVE AS feature on your computer. That way, if you change your mind about any revisions, you can cut and paste text from the original document.

CHECKLIST: DRAFTING

- ☐ Does your how-to writing fit your purpose and audience?
- ☐ Do you need to elaborate on any of the facts and details you have included?
- ☐ Did you present the steps in order?
- ☐ Did you use words that show how ideas are linked?
- ☐ Do your sentences flow together?

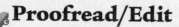

Proofread/Edit

After you have revised your explanatory writing, you will need to proofread it to correct errors in grammar, mechanics and usage, and spelling. Use these proofreading marks to mark errors on your draft.

PROOFREADING MARKS

⌗ new paragraph

∧ add

⌒ take out

≡ Make a capital letter.

/ Make a small letter.

🔤 Check the spelling.

⊙ Add a period.

4

Study the Model and Practice

Look at the proofreading corrections made on the draft below. What does the ℘ symbol mean? Why is the writer taking out the word *most* in the last paragraph?

REVISE

129 June Lane

Sayville, Maryland

21092

July 12, 20____

dear Joanna,

                                    We'll have a great time.
    I'm so excited you are coming to visit!

¶ Here are the directions to my apartment.
We can swim in the pool. Take Merrick Road
to the traffic light
north. Then, turn right on Planet Road.

   big white on the right left
Look for the school building. Turn on Elm

old wooden
Avenue and go over the bridge. Next, turn

right (SP) two   red brick
on June Lane and go too miles. Look for the

across from
apartment buildings at the park.

   (SP) fourth on the left
    I live in Building D. It's the forth building, the

one most closest to the pool. I'll be there!

best
              Your bestest friend,

Mariana

Then follow these strategies to proofread your draft:

- **Reread your revised paper several times.** Check for different types of errors each time.

- **Check for punctuation errors.** Be sure you used commas and end punctuation correctly.

- **Check each sentence for correct capitalization.** Be sure to use capitals for letter street names, city names, and people's names.

- **Check for correct grammar and usage.** Be sure you have written complete, grammatical sentences.

- **Check for spelling mistakes.** Read your paper from the bottom to the top, word for word, to spot errors more easily.

TECHNOLOGY TIP!
A spell-checker cannot catch words that are used incorrectly, such as homophones. For example, if you write *peace* instead of *piece*, the spell-checker will not point it out. You must also proofread your writing carefully.

CHECKLIST: BEFORE YOU PUBLISH
- [ ] Did you spell all the words correctly?
- [ ] Did you use commas correctly?
- [ ] Did you use capital letters where needed?
- [ ] Did you avoid grammar errors?

4

Publish and Present

After revising and editing, you may choose to publish your writing to share with others.

The writer used the Before You Publish checklist to help her review her letter to her friend. Read the letter and discuss it with a small group of classmates. Are the directions in the letter easy to understand and follow? Do you think the letter is ready to be sent? Why or why not?

129 June Lane
Sayville, Maryland 21092
July 12, 20__

Dear Joanna,

    I'm so excited you are coming to visit! We'll have a great time. We can swim in the pool.

    Here are the directions to my apartment. Take Merrick Road north to the traffic light. Then, turn right on Planet Road. Look for the big white school building on the right. Turn left on Elm Avenue and go over the old wooden bridge. Next, turn right on June Lane and go two miles. Look for the red brick apartment buildings across from the park.

    I live in Building D. It's the fourth building on the left, the one closest to the pool. I'll be there!

Your best friend,
Mariana

Practice

- Give your revised draft one more careful look.
- Make a neat final copy. Decide if you would like to include headings to help readers identify each step of your explanation.
- Draw maps, diagrams, or illustrations to go with your explanation.

After you publish, share your how-to writing with others. Use this rubric to help evaluate your published piece.

Writing Rubric: How-to Writing

Score	Description
4 **Excellent**	<ul><li>creates a focused explanation with clear details</li><li>explains the topic in an engaging manner and logical order</li><li>uses a personal style and demonstrates original knowledge</li><li>uses time-order and spatial-order words to make transitions</li><li>uses a variety of sentences that flow smoothly</li><li>is free or almost free of errors</li></ul>
3 **Good**	<ul><li>creates a solid explanation with clear details</li><li>introduces the topic and explanation in a logical order</li><li>uses a personal tone and shows new knowledge</li><li>includes some time-order and spatial-order words to make transitions</li><li>uses a variety of complete sentences</li><li>has minor errors that do not confuse the reader</li></ul>
2 **Fair**	<ul><li>tries to explain, but details may be unclear</li><li>presents some steps or ideas out of order</li><li>does not connect with readers</li><li>includes few time-order or spatial-order words to make transitions</li><li>uses only simple sentences that lack variety</li><li>makes frequent errors that confuse the reader</li><li>creates an incomplete explanation</li><li>does not include a clear beginning or show signs of logical order</li><li>does not use a personal voice and shows little knowledge of the topic</li><li>does not use transitions between ideas</li><li>uses run-on sentences and sentence fragments</li><li>makes serious and repeated errors</li></ul>
1 **Unsatisfactory**	<ul><li>creates an incomplete explanation</li><li>does not include a clear beginning or show signs of logical order</li><li>does not use a personal voice and shows little knowledge of the topic</li><li>does not use transitions between ideas</li><li>uses run-on sentences and sentence fragments</li><li>makes serious and repeated errors</li></ul>

4

TECHNOLOGY TIP!

Use available technology to share your writing.

- E-mail your published piece to your teacher or classmates.
- Display your writing on an electronic white board.
- Record it and save it as an audio file so others can listen to it on an mp3 player.

CHECKLIST: BEFORE YOU PUBLISH

- ☐ Who was my audience? Will my writing be clear to them?
- ☐ What was my purpose for writing? Did I organize my information so that my audience can understand it?
- ☐ Did I give my instructions in a logical step-by-step order?
- ☐ Did I include helpful facts and details that make the steps clear?
- ☐ Did I use time-order or spatial words to help make my instructions more precise?
- ☐ Did I check for mistakes in grammar?
- ☐ Did I correct all errors in capitalization and punctuation?

Part 4
WRITING
4.1 Text Types and Purposes

Standard 3

Lesson C
Write Narrative Texts

Narratives tell about real or made-up experiences and events. Writers often tell narratives to entertain. In this lesson you will learn how to write these narrative pieces.

● Personal Narrative

● Story

Personal Narrative

Have you ever told someone an interesting story about yourself? Your story was a personal narrative. A personal narrative brings to life a memorable event. It tells how the writer felt about the experience.

> **THINK AND WRITE**
>
> **Purpose** Why do you think people write personal narratives? Write a brief explanation in your journal. Also tell why other people like to read them.

Learning from Writers

Read the following example of personal narrative. What story does the writer tell? Why do you think he wanted to share his experience? As you read, look for phrases that show the writer's feelings.

Personal Narrative: Student Model

Misty and Me

I'll never forget the day my cat Misty had kittens. Cats like to have a warm, private place to have their kittens. So my dad and I made a cozy bed out of a large basket and an old baby blanket. We put it in my dark closet and left the door open a little. After that, we left to do an errand.

When we got back, we couldn't find Misty! I was very worried. I looked all over the house. Then I searched behind all the shelves in garage, but she was nowhere to be found.

"Dad," I moaned. "She's just… gone!"

"Don't give up, Jeff. She'll come out when she's ready," Dad comforted me.

I was searching the yard when I spotted her. She just appeared from the shadowy woods behind our house. In her mouth she was carrying a tiny new kitten! She had had her kittens outside.

When I thought more about it, I wasn't too surprised. Misty had always been very independent!

—Jeff Andrews

Practice

1. **Thinking Like a Reader** How did the author of "Misty and Me" feel when he found that his cat was missing?

2. **Thinking Like a Writer** What words did the author of "Misty and Me" use that help you understand how he felt?

Common Core State Standards Literacy Handbook

Features of Personal Narratives

A **personal narrative** is a form of writing that shares your personal experiences, including what you did and how you felt about your experiences. A good personal narrative includes the following.

Personal Experience

Reread "Misty and Me." Whom is this narrative about?

> I'll never forget the day my cat Misty had kittens.

The narrative is about the author. In a personal narrative, you write about something that happened to you.

I Point of View

When you write about yourself, you tell a story from your point of view, using the word *I*. You share your thoughts and feelings with the audience. Notice the *I* point of view in the sentence below. How do you think the author felt?

> When we got back, we couldn't find Misty! I was very worried.

Beginning, Middle, and End

A good personal narrative catches the reader's attention right from the start. The beginning also introduces the situation, or the experience, and the characters that the narrator will tell about. This beginning makes the reader wonder why this day was unforgettable. It introduces the situation: the day Misty had kittens.

> I'll never forget the day my cat Misty had kittens.

The middle of a personal narrative tells about the important events and details, often in the order that they happened naturally.

A good conclusion, or ending, is just as important as a good beginning. The ending might tell how the author felt or what he or she learned from the experience. A good ending finishes the personal narrative in a way that makes sense.

> When I thought more about it, I wasn't too surprised. Misty had always been very independent!

Transitions: Time-order Words and Phrases

To help your readers clearly understand your experience, you need to tell about events in a logical sequence, or order. Use time-order words and phrases, such as *first*, *the following day*, and *finally*.

The time-order phrase that the author used is underlined below.

> After that, we left to do an errand.

Concrete and Sensory Details

Writers help readers visualize the events and people in a personal narrative by using concrete words and phrases as well as sensory details. Concrete words are specific and vivid, rather than general or vague. They make the details of your narrative clear. Sensory details help a reader see, feel, smell, taste, or hear what you are writing about.

Compare these two sentences. Notice how the second is more descriptive. The details the author uses to describe the bed are underlined.

> So my dad and I made a bed.

> So my dad and I made a <u>cozy</u> bed out of a <u>large</u> basket and an <u>old</u> <u>baby</u> blanket.

Create a Features Chart

1. List the features of a personal narrative.

2. Reread a familiar personal narrative.

3. Write one example of each feature in the writing.

4. What did you like about the personal narrative?

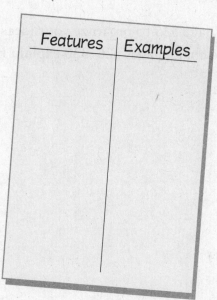

Features | Examples

Writing Process

Now you are ready to write your own personal narrative. Follow the steps of the writing process to develop your writing.

- Prewrite
- Draft
- Revise
- Edit
- Publish and Present

Prewrite

A personal narrative is a true story about yourself. Writing a personal narrative gives you a good chance to share a story about your own experience.

Turn to page 325 to organize your ideas for your personal narrative into a sequence chart. Pages 326-330 explain how to fill in the sequence chart.

Name _____

Sequence Chart

Practice

Use the sequence chart to record the events of your personal narrative in order.

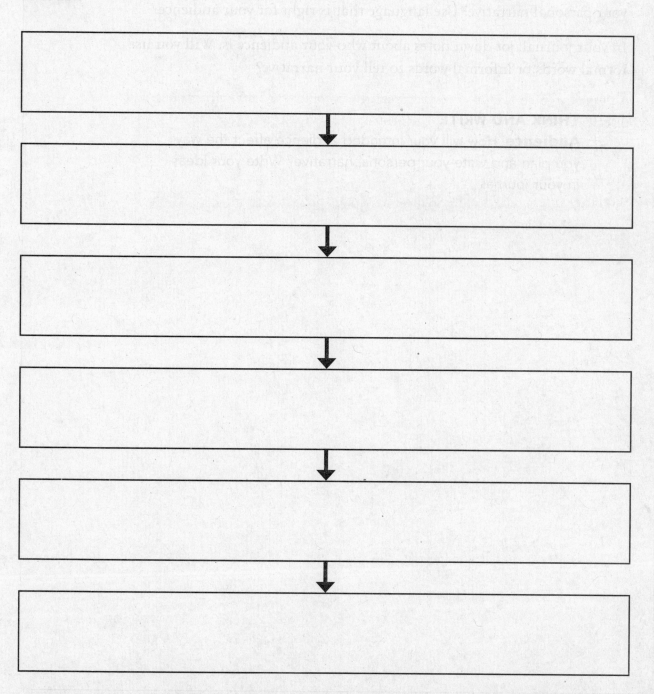

Study the Model and Practice

As you're prewriting a personal narrative, it's important to consider the following.

Purpose and Audience

The purpose of writing a personal narrative is to express your thoughts and feelings about an experience. It is also to entertain your readers, or audience.

Before writing, you need to think about your audience. Who will be reading your personal narrative? Use language that is right for your audience.

In your journal, jot down notes about who your audience is. Will you use formal words or informal words to tell your narrative?

> **THINK AND WRITE**
> **Audience** How will your intended audience affect the way you plan and write your personal narrative? Write your ideas in your journal.

Common Core State Standards Literacy Handbook

Choose a Topic

Start by **brainstorming** a list of memorable experiences that have happened to you. Think about which topic would be most interesting for your readers.

After choosing your topic, **explore ideas** by making a list of events. Also list some of your thoughts and feelings about them. Later, you will organize these ideas.

A Vacation Surprise

Ran into the water
Something amazing happened
Not too many people on beach or in water
Noticed something swimming toward me
Water was calm and clear
Got out of the water
Thought it was a shark
Saw that it was really a dolphin
It wasn't afraid of swimmers
The dolphin kept returning
A reporter interviewed me

4

Organize: Sequence

The events in a personal narrative happen in a certain order, or sequence. To plan your narrative, you can use a sequence-of-events chart. Not all your ideas may be necessary in order to tell your story. What ideas from her list did this writer leave out of her chart?

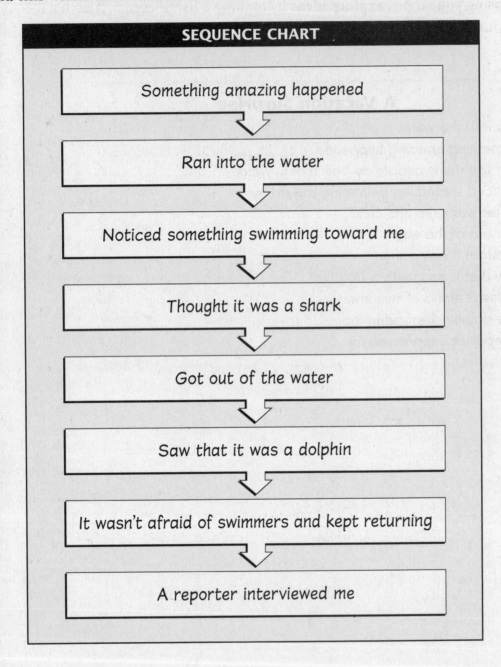

SEQUENCE CHART

Something amazing happened

Ran into the water

Noticed something swimming toward me

Thought it was a shark

Got out of the water

Saw that it was a dolphin

It wasn't afraid of swimmers and kept returning

A reporter interviewed me

Research
Writer's Resources

You may have to do research to get more information from other people who shared the experience you are recounting for your personal narrative. First, make a list of questions. Then decide what resources you need in order to answer your questions.

What Else Do I Need to Know?	Where Can I Find the Information?
How long did the dolphin keep returning? What kind of dolphin was it?	Check my journal. E-mail the reporter who interviewed me.

Conduct an Interview

An interview is a good way to find out what others thought and felt about the experience you are recounting. An interview is really a conversation. One person asks questions, and the other person answers. An interview can take place in person, in writing, on the telephone, or by e-mail.

Strategies for Interviewing

- Know what you want to ask. Write your questions.
- Send the questions ahead of time. The person you interview will have time to think about answers.
- Take notes so you remember the answers.
- Be polite and friendly. Thank the person at the end.

Study Personal Records

Photographs, journals, and souvenirs can also help you remember any details you may have forgotten. Look for specific details in photos or journal entries that will help you write clearly and specifically. Try to remember sensory details of color, sound, or smell. Using these details in your writing will make the event more real to your audience.

Use Your Research

New information gathered from your research can go into your sequence-of-events chart. This writer learned something important from her interview with the newspaper reporter. How did she change her chart?

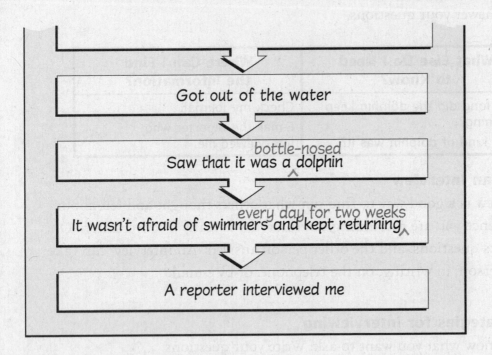

Got out of the water

Saw that it was a dolphin   bottle-nosed

It wasn't afraid of swimmers and kept returning   every day for two weeks

A reporter interviewed me

CHECKLIST: PREWRITING

☐ Have you listed your experiences?

☐ Have you thought about your purpose and audience?

☐ Have you chosen a topic and explored ideas about it?

☐ Are your ideas organized into a chart?

☐ Have you checked the order of events?

☐ Do you need to do any research?

Draft

Now that you have gathered your ideas for a personal narrative, you are ready to begin drafting. When you write a first draft, you get your ideas down on paper. Don't worry about making mistakes. You can fix them later when you revise and edit.

Study the Model and Practice

As you're drafting your personal narrative, it's important to consider the following.

Write a Strong Beginning

A strong beginning gets readers interested in your narrative and sets up the situation you are writing about. At the beginning of your personal narrative, introduce when and where the event or experience took place. Let your readers know that this is a story about something that happened to you by using the word *I*.

Look at how this writer started her draft. Who is it about? Where did it take place? How does the writer make you want to keep reading?

4

> <u>I used to feel that nothing exciting would ever happen to me I don't feel that way anymore. While I was visiting my grandmother in Florida, something amazing finally happened. I will never forget that amazing vacation.</u>
>
> It was the second day of our vacation. We got to the beach early. I dropped my stuff and ran into the warm water. I noticed something silently moving toward me. I thought it was a shark. I backed out of the water.
>
> "Grandma!" I screamed. "Shark!"
>
> I saw that it was a bottle-nosed dolphin. It wasn't afraid of the swimmers. In fact, it returned every day for two weeks.
>
> A reporter heard about the dolphin. The reporter interviewed me. a picture appeared in the newspaper It was such an exciting experience.

Use Dialogue and Descriptive Details

Throughout your draft, use dialogue and descriptive details. Dialogue can express how you or other characters felt. Use quotation marks to show the words a character actually said. Concrete words and sensory details give readers a clear picture of the events in your narrative.

This writer used dialogue to show that she was afraid. She uses details to describe when and where the events took place. Identify the details the writer uses. Which detail describes what she felt? Which detail describes what she heard?

It was the <u>second</u> day of our vacation. We got to the beach <u>early</u>. I dropped my stuff and ran into the <u>warm</u> water. I noticed something <u>silently</u> moving toward me. I thought it was a shark. I backed out of the water.

"Grandma!" I screamed. "Shark!"

I saw that it was a <u>bottle-nosed</u> dolphin. It wasn't afraid of the swimmers. In fact, it returned every day for two weeks.

Write a Good Conclusion

Finish your draft with a sentence or two that tells how the event or experience ended and how this experience affected you, such as the underlined conclusion here. Your conclusion should give your readers a sense of closure, or completeness.

I used to feel that nothing exciting would ever happen to me I don't feel that way anymore. While I was visiting my grandmother in Florida, something amazing finally happened. I will never forget that amazing vacation.

It was the second day of our vacation. We got to the beach early. I dropped my stuff and ran into the warm water. I noticed something silently moving toward me. I thought it was a shark. I backed out of the water.

"Grandma!" I screamed. "Shark!"

I saw that it was a bottle-nosed dolphin. It wasn't afraid of the swimmers. In fact, it returned every day for two weeks.

A reporter heard about the dolphin. The reporter interviewed me. a picture appeared in the newspaper It was such an exciting experience.

4

TECHNOLOGY TIP!

Give your document a detailed name that you will remember.
You may wish to include the word *draft* in the name.

CHECKLIST: DRAFTING

- ☐ Does your writing fit your purpose and audience?
- ☐ Have you used the word *I* to show that the events happened to you?
- ☐ Have you included your thoughts and feelings?
- ☐ Does your narrative have a clear beginning, middle, and end?
- ☐ Are the events in a logical order?
- ☐ Do you give details that will help readers feel as though they had been there?

Revise

Now that you have completed your draft, it is time to revise it. Revising offers a chance to make sure your ideas are clear. Writers revise their writing before it is published to make sure their readers can understand the message. When you revise, reread your draft to add details, to delete unnecessary ideas or words, to substitute more precise language for overused words and phrases, or to rearrange ideas to make them clearer. Then have a partner review your draft and give you feedback.

Study the Model and Practice

As you're revising your personal narrative, it's important to consider the following.

Elaborate: Add Descriptive Details

One way to improve your writing is to elaborate. When you elaborate, you add important ideas and details that might be missing from your writing. When you revise your personal narrative, you may need to add more **concrete words or phrase**s to help readers picture what happened. Look for places where you can use **sensory details** to help readers see, hear, feel, taste, or smell what you are writing about.

The details that the writer added let the reader know how she feels and describe more clearly how she moved.

> was afraid and quickly
> I thought it was a shark. I backed out of the water.

The writer used more specific, concrete words to show that she was with her grandmother at the beach. This language helps the reader better understand her writing.

> My grandmother and I
> We got to the beach early.

Transition Words and Phrases

When you are writing, it is important to use words that connect ideas and help the events of your story to flow logically. In a personal narrative, you need to find words that will help you tell the story events in order. Use time-order words and phrases to transition from one event to the next.

At first,
I thought it was a shark. I backed out of the water.
Then,
I saw that it was a bottle-nosed dolphin.

was afraid and quickly

TRANSITION WORDS

first	yesterday	finally
next	before	one day
then	after	tomorrow
later	last	a long time ago
this morning	as soon as	

Better Sentences

As you continue to revise your draft, check your sentences to make sure they fit together well. Read the sentences aloud. How do they sound? Have you included different types of sentences? Using compound subjects and compound predicates can help your sentences flow better.

Sometimes you can combine two short sentences to make one sentence that is longer and more interesting.

A reporter heard

about the dolphin.

The reporter

interviewed me.

A reporter heard

about the dolphin

and interviewed me.

Peer Conferencing

Take a break from your writing. Give your draft to your partner to read. Read your partner's writing. Someone else may have some fresh ideas or suggestions you haven't thought of yourself.

As you read your partner's draft, use these prompts to guide your review.

> ☐ **Are the features of a personal narrative included in your partner's work?**
> - personal experience
> - I point of view
> - interesting beginning, middle, and end
> - sequence that makes sense
> - descriptive details
> - time-order words
>
> ☐ **Make sure to tell your partner what's good about the piece as well as what needs improvement.**

4

When you revise your personal narrative, you can use your partner's comments and suggestions to help you decide what changes need to be made. Look at the changes this writer made after talking to his partner.

Good beginning!

I used to feel that nothing exciting would ever happen to me I don't feel that way anymore. While I was visiting my grandmother in Florida,

This would make a good ending

something amazing finally happened. I will never forget that amazing vacation

It was the second day of our vacation. We got to the beach early. I dropped my stuff and ran intothe water. I noticed something moving

What did it look like?

toward me. I thought it was a shark. I backed out of the water. I saw that it was a bottle-nosed dolphin. It wasn't afraid of the swimmers. In fact, it returned every day for two weeks.

"Grandma!" I screamed. "Shark!"

Can you tell me more about the picture?

A reporter heard about the dolphin. The reporter interviewed me. a picture appeared in the newspaper It was such and exciting experience.

Vacation Surprise

I used to feel that nothing exciting would ever happen to me I don't feel that way anymore. While I was visiting my grandmother in Florida, something amazing finally happened. I will never forget that amazing vacation

It was the second day of our vacation. We got to the beach early. I dropped my stuff and ran intothe water. I noticed something moving toward me. I thought it was a shark. I backed out of the water. I saw that it was a bottle-nosed dolphin. It wasn't afraid of the swimmers. In fact, it returned every day for two weeks.

My grandmother and I
bag and towel
Suddenly   huge
At first,   was afraid and gickly
Then,

"Grandma!" I screamed. "Shark!"

A reporter heard about the dolphin. The reporter interviewed me. a picture appeared in the newspaper It was such and exciting experience.

and
of the dolphin and me

CHECKLIST: REVISING

☐ Does your personal narrative fit your purpose and audience?

☐ Do you need to add dialogue or descriptive details?

☐ Did you present events in sequence?

☐ Did you use transition words or phrases?

☐ Do your sentences flow together?

☐ Did you add a good title?

Proofread/Edit

After you have revised your personal narrative, you will need to proofread it to correct errors in grammar, mechanics and usage, and spelling. Use these proofreading marks to mark errors on your draft.

PROOFREADING MARKS

⌗ new paragraph

∧ add

℘ take out

≡ Make a capital letter.

/ Make a small letter.

⑤Ⓟ Check the spelling.

⊙ Add a period.

Study the Model and Practice

Look at the proofreading corrections made on the draft shown below. What does the ≡ symbol mean? When does the writer use that symbol?

PROOFREAD

Vacation Surprise

I used to feel that nothing exciting would

but

ever happen to me I don't feel that way

anymore. While I was visiting my grandmother in

Florida, something amazing finally happened. I

will never forget that amazing vacation!

My grandmother and I

It was the second day of our vacation. ~~We~~

bag and towel

got to the beach early. I dropped my ~~stuff~~ and

Suddenly huge

ran intothe water. I noticed something moving

At first, was afraid and qickly

toward me. I thought it was a shark. I backed

Then,

out of the water. I saw that it was a bottle-

nosed dolphin. It wasn't afraid of the swimmers.

In fact, it returned every day for two weeks.

"Grandma!" I screamed. "Shark!"

and

A reporter heard about the dolphin. ~~The~~

of the dolphin and me

~~reporter~~ interviewed me. a picture appeared

≡

in the newspaper It was such and exciting

experience.

Then follow these strategies to proofread your draft:

- **Reread your revised paper several times.** Check for different types of errors each time.

- **Check for punctuation errors.** Be sure you used commas and end punctuation correctly.

- **Check each sentence for correct capitalization.** Be sure to use capitals for street names, city names, and people's names.

- **Check for correct grammar and usage.** Be sure your sentences are complete and grammatically correct.

- **Check for spelling mistakes.** Read your paper from the bottom to the top, word for word, to spot errors more easily.

TECHNOLOGY TIP!
Spell-checkers don't always find repeated or missing words.
Read your draft carefully to be sure you didn't type any words
twice or leave any words out.

CHECKLIST: PROOFREADING
- ☐ Did you spell all the words correctly?
- ☐ Did you use commas and end punctuation correctly?
- ☐ Did you use capital letters where needed?
- ☐ Did you avoid errors in grammar and usage?

Publish and Present

After revising and editing, you may choose to publish your writing to share with others. The writer used the Before You Publish checklist on page 346 to look over her writing one last time. Read "Vacation Surprise" and write about it in your journal. Do you think the piece was ready for publishing? Give reasons for your ideas.

Vacation Surprise

I used to feel that nothing exciting would ever happen to me, but I don't feel that way anymore. While I was visiting my grandmother in Florida, something amazing finally happened.

It was the second day of our vacation. My grandmother and I got to the beach early. I dropped my bag and towel and ran into the warm water. Suddenly I noticed something huge moving silently toward me. At first, I thought it was a shark. I was afraid and quickly backed out of the water.

"Grandma!" I screamed. "Shark!"

Then, I saw that it was a bottle-nosed dolphin. It wasn't afraid of the swimmers. In fact, it returned every day for two weeks.

A local reporter heard about the dolphin and interviewed me. A picture of the dolphin and me appeared in the newspaper. It was such an exciting experience. I will never forget that amazing vacation!

—Jasmine Wright

Practice

- Check your revised draft one more time.
- Make a neat final copy.
- Add a border or decorative art.
- Place your narrative in a scrapbook.
- Add photos, drawings, or postcards to your scrapbook.

After you publish, share your personal narrative with others. You may wish to post it on a class Web site or read it aloud. Use this rubric to help evaluate your published piece.

Writing Rubric: Personal Narrative

Score	Description
4 **Excellent**	• tells about a personal experience and includes thoughts and feelings • includes a strong beginning, middle, and end • conveys a strong personal message • uses a variety of transitions • uses a variety of words in a natural way • uses a variety of sentences that flow • is free or almost free of errors
3 **Good**	• tells about a personal experience and includes some thoughts and feelings • presents details in the correct order • makes an effort to share a message • uses some transitions • uses appropriate words • uses a variety of complete sentences • has minor errors that do not confuse the reader
2 **Fair**	• tells about a personal experience but loses focus • includes events told out of order • shows little personal involvement • uses one or two transitions • does not use descriptive words or uses words poorly • uses only simple sentences • makes frequent errors that confuse the reader • does not share a personal experience
1 **Unsatisfactory**	• tells events out of order and is confusing • does not express feelings or connect with readers • does not use transitions • uses words not related to the purpose • uses run-on sentences and sentence fragments • makes serious and repeated errors

4

CHECKLIST: BEFORE YOU PUBLISH

☐ Who was my audience? Did I write in a way that will interest them?

☐ What was my purpose? Will the reader know how I felt?

☐ Did I use the *I* point of view to tell about a personal experience?

☐ Did I begin and end my narrative in an interesting way?

☐ Did I choose time-order words carefully to help make the sequence of events clear?

☐ Are my sentences varied? Do they fit together well?

☐ Did I begin and end all my sentences correctly?

☐ Did I combine sentences when I could to make my writing flow better?

Story

Have you ever written a story using your imagination? If so, your story probably had characters, a setting, and a plot. Stories are narratives, and their purpose is usually to entertain readers.

> **THINK AND WRITE**
>
> **Purpose** Why do you think people write stories? Write a brief explanation in your journal. Also tell why other people like to read them.

Learning from Writers

Read this example of a story. Who is the main character? Where does the story take place? Think about what happens in the story and how the story ends.

Story: Student Model

A Dream Come True

Jimmy Martinez always wanted a pony. Where he lived, in the Arizona desert, it seemed as if everyone had a pony.

One day, Jimmy saw a little pony on the pathway down the canyon. A rock had come loose and pinned its back leg against the canyon wall. The pony was stuck, and it neighed unhappily. Jimmy inched down the path, speaking quietly to the brown, spotted pony. When he reached the pony, he leaned his back against the rock and pushed with all his strength. The rock moved just enough to free the pony's leg. Jimmy took off his belt and looped it around the pony's neck.

Jimmy and the pony walked up the path together. When they reached home, Dad came out to see them.

"Can I keep him?" begged Jimmy.

"Someone may call about him," said Dad. "If so, you will have to give him back." They cleaned and bandaged the pony's leg. Weeks went by, and the pony's leg healed, but no one called. Dad said that Jimmy could have the pony.

"I will call him Dream," said Jimmy, "because he is my dream come true."

—Tommy Ortega

Practice

1. **Thinking Like a Reader** In "A Dream Come True," how does Jimmy rescue the pony?

2. **Thinking Like a Writer** What word does Tommy Ortega use to describe how Jimmy asked if he could keep the pony?

Features of a Story

A story is a narrative that a writer creates from his or her imagination. A good story has these traits.

Characters

The actions and thoughts of characters make up a story. What do these sentences tell about Jimmy's thoughts in "A Dream Come True"?

> Jimmy Martinez always wanted a pony.

Jimmy has always wanted a pony. The story is about how he finds and gets his very own pony.

Plot

Every story has a plot. The plot involves a problem that needs to be solved. In Tommy Ortega's story, the problem is how Jimmy rescues a pony and whether or not he will get to keep it. How is the problem solved in "A Dream Come True"?

> Weeks went by, and the pony's leg healed, but no one called.
> Dad said that Jimmy could have the pony.

Setting

A story's setting is the time and place in which the action occurs. Details about the setting help the reader create a picture in his or her mind. What is the setting of this story?

> Where he lived, in the Arizona desert, it seemed as if everyone had a pony. One day, Jimmy saw a little pony stuck on the pathway down the canyon.

Beginning, Middle, and End

The beginning of a story usually introduces the characters, the setting, and a problem. The middle tells the events that result from the problem in order. The ending solves the problem and provides a logical conclusion to the story.

Writers use a variety of time-order words and phrases, such as *first*, *the following day*, and *finally* to **transition** from one event to the next in their stories.

The transition phrase the author uses is underlined in the passage below.

> Jimmy and the pony walked up the path together. <u>When they reached home</u>, Dad came out to see them.

Dialogue

Dialogue is the exact words of a character. It often includes a tag line that tells how those words are spoken. Dialogue can be used to reveal how the characters feel. What does this dialogue reveal about the character?

> "Can I keep him?" begged Jimmy.

The exact words of the character show the question he asked about keeping the horse. The word *begged* in the tag line shows that he really wanted the pony.

Description: Concrete Words and Sensory Details

Writers help readers visualize the events and characters in a story by using concrete words and phrases and sensory details. Concrete words are specific and vivid, rather than general or vague. They make the details of your story clear. Sensory details help a reader see, feel, smell, taste, or hear what you are writing about.

Compare these two sentences. Notice how the second sentence is more specific. See how the underlined concrete nouns, vivid verbs, and sensory details make it more descriptive.

> Jimmy moved down the path, speaking to the animal.

> Jimmy inched down the path, speaking quietly to the brown, spotted pony.

Create a Story Map

1. Reread a familiar story.

2. Draw a story map. List the title of the story, the setting, the characters, and the problem.

3. Then list each event separately.

4. At the bottom, write the solution to the problem.

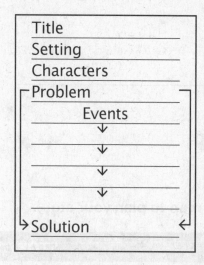

Writing Process

Now you are ready to write your own story. Follow the steps of the writing process to develop your writing.

- ⬤ **Prewrite**
- ⬤ **Draft**
- ⬤ **Revise**
- ⬤ **Edit**
- ⬤ **Publish and Present**

Prewrite

A story is a form of writing that is created from the author's imagination. Writing a story gives you the opportunity to share your creativity and imagination with others.

Turn to page 352 to create a story map for your story. Pages 353–356 provides more information on the types of details to add to the story map.

Name _____

Story Map

Practice

Use the story map to plan your story.

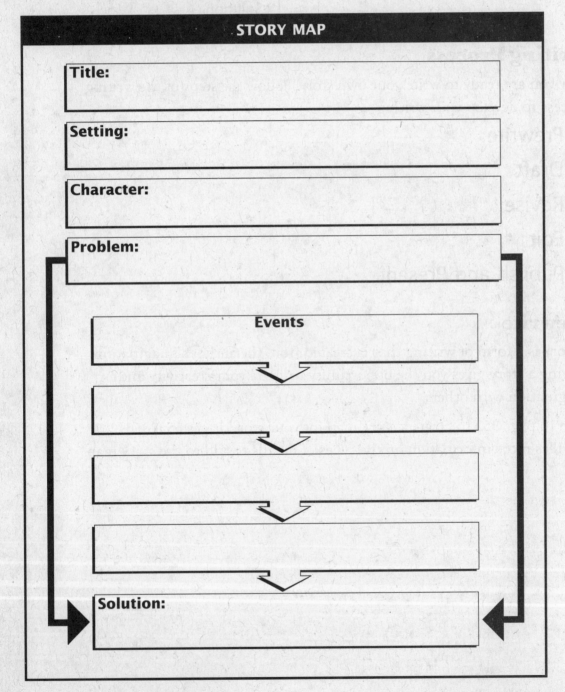

STORY MAP

Title:

Setting:

Character:

Problem:

Events

Solution:

Study the Model and Practice

To begin writing your story, you will consider the following.

Purpose and Audience

The purpose of writing a story is to entertain your audience. It is also a way to express your thoughts and ideas through a real or imaginary situation or topic.

Before writing, you need to think about your audience. Who will be reading your story? How will you make your story fun for your audience to read? Jot your ideas down in your journal.

> **THINK AND WRITE**
> **Audience** Who might read your story? Write about how you will create characters and events that will capture your reader's attention.

Choose a Topic

Begin by **brainstorming** a list of ideas or situations that might make an interesting plot, or story line. Remember that a good story should include a problem and show how that problem is solved.

After you have chosen the plot for your story, **explore ideas** by listing the events that will take place, as well as ideas for the characters and setting.

> Girl and her aunt
> Traveling by dog sled on a frozen lake
> Saw something moving on the ice
> Snowstorm was starting
> Man took the rope
> Man was holding onto hole in ice
> Aunt tied rope to dog sled
> Dogs pulled man from lake
> Man thanked them
> Man gave them bag of gold

Organize: Story Map

A story needs to have a clear beginning, middle, and end so that the audience can understand the order of the events. To plan your story, you can use a story map. How did this writer use her story map to organize all the elements of her story?

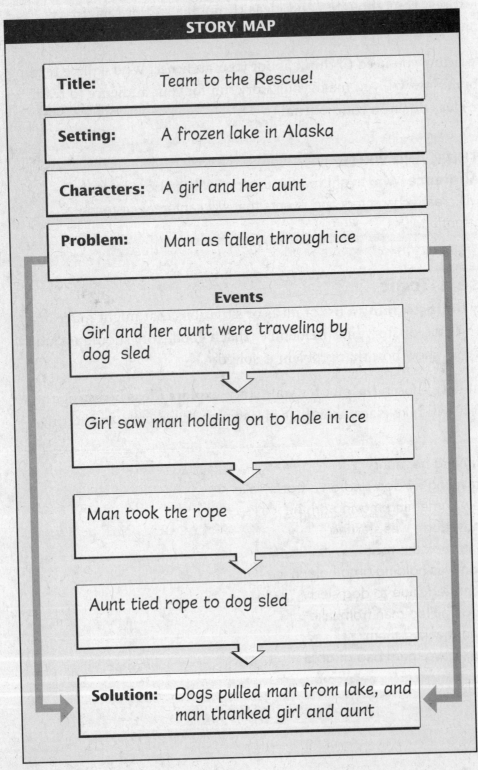

STORY MAP

Title: Team to the Rescue!

Setting: A frozen lake in Alaska

Characters: A girl and her aunt

Problem: Man as fallen through ice

Events

Girl and her aunt were traveling by dog sled

Girl saw man holding on to hole in ice

Man took the rope

Aunt tied rope to dog sled

Solution: Dogs pulled man from lake, and man thanked girl and aunt

Common Core State Standards Literacy Handbook

Research
Writer's Resources

You may wish to do research to make your story more entertaining and realistic. Make a list of questions and decide what resources may help you answer them.

What Else Do I Need to Know?	Where Can I Find the Information?
Is there a more precise word for *took* I can use?	Look up *take* in a thesaurus.
Can I use the word *mushing* to mean "traveling by dog sled"?	Look up *mush* in the dictionary.

Study a Thesaurus

A thesaurus is a book that lists synonyms, or words with the same or similar meanings. It also lists antonyms, or words with opposite meanings. A thesaurus can also be on a computer. Use a thesaurus to find specific, concrete words and sensory details.

Use a Dictionary

A dictionary lists words in alphabetical order. In each listing, you will find the pronunciation of the word as well as one or more definitions, example sentences, and parts of speech. You can use a dictionary to make sure you are using words correctly and to check their spelling.

Use Your Research

The new information that you gathered from your research can be added to your story map. How did this writer use information from a dictionary and a thesaurus to change her story map?

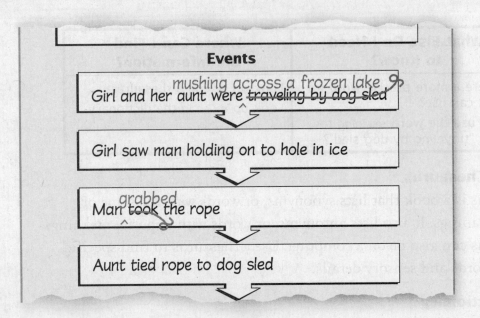

Events

Girl and her aunt were ~~traveling by dog sled~~ *mushing across a frozen lake*

↓

Girl saw man holding on to hole in ice

↓

Man ~~took~~ *grabbed* the rope

↓

Aunt tied rope to dog sled

CHECKLIST: PUBLISHING

☐ Have you thought about your purpose and audience?

☐ Have you listed story ideas from your imagination?

☐ Have you chosen a topic or situation and explored your ideas about it?

☐ Have you selected an interesting setting and characters?

☐ Are your ideas organized in a chart?

☐ Do you need to do any research?

Draft

Now that you have gathered your ideas for a story, you are ready to begin drafting. When you write a first draft, you get your ideas down on paper. Don't worry about making mistakes. You can fix them later when you revise and edit.

Study the Model and Practice

As you're drafting, it's important to consider the following.

Write a Strong Beginning

At the beginning of your story, introduce the setting, characters, and problem. A strong beginning gets readers interested in the situation, or problem, your character will face.

Look at how this writer started her draft. What is the setting? Who are the characters? What problem do they face?

> Beth and her Aunt Sue were mushing across a frozen lake. There wasnt much daylight left, and Beth wanted to get back to camp before dark. She was tired. Sue was tired.
>
> All of a sudden, Beth saw something moving on the ice. She shouted, pointing ahead. They saw a man holding on to the edge of a hole in the ice.
>
> The man grabbed the rope, and Aunt Sue tied the other end to the sled. Then she said, pull!
>
> The dogs barked and pulled hard. Beth gripped the reins. The team pulled the man free just as the ice split open. "Your safe now, Beth said. "Thank you!" the man said.

Use Dialogue and Descriptive Details

As you continue your draft, write the events in the order they happened. Use dialogue to move the plot along and to express how the characters feel.

Good description helps your readers visualize your story. Use concrete and sensory details to give readers a clear picture of the events in your story. Use specific nouns, vivid verbs, and sensory details that tell how something looks, sounds, feels, smells, or tastes.

This writer used dialogue and description to move the plot along and show how characters respond to the situation, or problem.

Beth and her Aunt Sue were mushing across a frozen lake. There wasnt much daylight left, and Beth wanted to get back to camp before dark. She was tired. Sue was tired.

All of a sudden, Beth saw something moving on the ice. She shouted, pointing ahead. They saw a man holding on to the edge of a hole in the ice.

The man grabbed the rope, and Aunt Sue tied the other end to the sled. Then she said, pull!

The dogs barked and pulled hard. Beth gripped the reins. The team pulled the man free just as the ice split open. "Your safe now," Beth said. "Thank you!" the man said.

Write a Good Conclusion

Finish your story by telling how the problem was solved. Your conclusion should give your readers a sense of closure, or completeness.

Beth and her Aunt Sue were mushing across a frozen lake. There wasnt much daylight left, and Beth wanted to get back to camp before dark. She was tired. Sue was tired.

All of a sudden, Beth saw something moving on the ice. She shouted, pointing ahead. They saw a man holding on to the edge of a hole in the ice.

The man grabbed the rope, and Aunt Sue tied the other end to the sled. Then she said, pull!

The dogs barked and pulled hard. Beth gripped the reins. The team pulled the man free just as the ice split open. "Your safe now," Beth said. "Thank you!" the man said.

TECHNOLOGY TIP!

Find out how to adjust line spacing on your computer. It's a good idea to double-space your draft so that you will leave more room to make corrections if you print your story for reviewing later.

CHECKLIST: DRAFTING

- ☐ Does your writing fit your purpose and audience?
- ☐ Have you included interesting characters for your story?
- ☐ Have you described the setting?
- ☐ Does your plot have a clear beginning, middle, and end?
- ☐ Does your story include a problem that is solved?

4

Revise

Now that you have completed your draft, it is time to revise it. Revising is a chance to make sure your ideas are clear. Writers revise their writing before it is published to make sure their readers can understand the message. When you revise, reread your draft to add details, to delete unnecessary ideas or words, to substitute more precise language for overused words and phrases, or to rearrange ideas to make them clearer. Then have a partner review your draft and give you feedback.

Study the Model and Practice

As you're revising, it's important to consider the following.

Elaborate: Add Concrete and Sensory Details

One way to improve your writing is to elaborate. When you elaborate, you add important ideas and details that might be missing from your writing. When you revise your story, you may need to add more concrete words or phrases that specifically describe your characters, setting, and the events. Look for places where you can use sensory details to help readers see, hear, feel, taste, or smell what you are writing about.

The writer added concrete and sensory details to tell the reader more about the setting.

> One cold winter afternoon,
> Beth and her Aunt Sue were mushing across a
> in Alaska
> frozen lake.

Word Choice: Dialogue

When you are writing, be sure to choose words that will help you tell an interesting and vivid story.

In a story, you can use dialogue to tell a reader's exact words. When you use dialogue, select words that will help readers understand the feelings, thoughts, and reactions of characters when they speak.

"Look, Aunt Sue!"
She shouted, pointing ahead.

WORDS THAT DESCRIBE THE DIALOGUE

replied	whispered	begged
responded	asked	chuckled
cried	grasped	pleaded
shouted	exclaimed	

4

Better Sentences: Transitions

While continuing to revise your draft, review your sentences to make certain they work well together. Read the sentences aloud. Do the events in the story flow smoothly from one to another? Do the sentences vary in length and in structure?

> The dogs barked and pulled hard. Beth gripped
> the reins. ^Finally The team pulled the man free just as the
> ice split open.

TRANSITION WORDS

first	yesterday	finally
next	before	one day
then	after	tomorrow
later	last	a long time ago
this morning	as soon as	

Peer Conferencing

Step back from the story you are writing. Ask a partner to read a copy of your first draft. In exchange, you can read your partner's story. This way, both of you can offer new ideas about each other's work.

As you read your partner's draft, use these prompts to guide your review.

☐ **Are the features of a story included in your partner's work?**
- interesting beginning, middle, and end
- well-developed characters
- a plot with a problem to be solved
- a well-described setting
- dialogue
- transition words and phrases

☐ **Make sure to tell your partner what's good about the piece as well as what needs improvement.**

When you revise your story, you can use your partner's comments and suggestions to help you decide what changes need to be made. Look at the changes this writer made after talking to her partner.

This beginning makes me want to read more!

The plot isn't clear here. You need to add more details.

Can you make the ending more interesting? Maybe you could add more dialogue.

Team to the Rescue!

Beth and her Aunt Sue were mushing across a frozen lake. There wasnt much daylight left, and Beth wanted to get back to camp before dark. She was tired. Sue was tired.

All of a sudden, Beth saw something moving on the ice. She shouted, pointing ahead. They saw a man holding on to the edge of a hole in the ice.

The man grabbed the rope, and Aunt Sue tied the other end to the sled. Then she said, pull!

The dogs barked and pulled hard. Beth gripped the reins. The team pulled the man free just as the ice split open. "Your safe now, Beth said. "Thank you!" the man said.

Team to the Rescue!

One cold winter afternoon,
Beth and her Aunt Sue were mushing across
in Alaska
a frozen lake. There wasnt much daylight left, and

Beth wanted to get back to camp before dark.
and   were
She was tired? Sue was tired.

All of a sudden, Beth saw something moving
"Look, Aunt Sue!"   When they got closer,
on the ice. She shouted, pointing ahead. They saw
clinging
a man holding on to the edge of a hole in the ice.
Aunt Sue slid a thick rope across the ice.
The man grabbed the rope, and Aunt Sue tied
cried
the other end to the sled. Then she said, pull!

The dogs barked and pulled hard. Beth

gripped the reins. The team pulled the man free
exclaimed
just as the ice split open. "Your safe now, Beth said.
gasped
"Thank you!" the man said.   "You saved my life!"

TECHNOLOGY TIP!
Review your draft for logical order. Do the ideas flow smoothly?
If not, try moving paragraphs or sentences around by cutting
and pasting text.

CHECKLIST: REVISING

☐ Does your story fit your purpose and audience?

☐ Did you create interesting dialogue that makes your characters seem like real people?

☐ Did you use concrete words and sensory details that provide readers with a clear picture of the setting?

☐ Did you create a plot with a beginning, a middle, and an end?

☐ Did you use transition words and phrases?

Proofread/Edit

After you have revised your story, you will need to proofread it to correct errors in grammar, mechanics and usage, and spelling. Use these proofreading marks to mark errors on your draft.

PROOFREADING MARKS

⌗ new paragraph

∧ add

℘ take out

≡ Make a capital letter.

∕ Make a small letter.

⑤ℙ Check the spelling.

⊙ Add a period.

4

Study the Model and Practice

Look at the proofreading corrections made on the draft shown below. What does the ⌗ symbol mean? When does the writer use that symbol?

PROOFREAD

Team to the Rescue!

One cold winter afternoon,
Beth and her Aunt Sue were mushing across
in Alaska
a frozen lake. There wasn't much daylight left, and

Beth wanted to get back to camp before dark.
and   were
She was tired? Sue was tired.

All of a sudden, Beth saw something moving
"Look, Aunt Sue!"   When they got closer,
on the ice. She shouted, pointing ahead. They saw
clinging
a man holding on to the edge of a hole in the ice.
Aunt Sue slid a thick rope across the ice.
The man grabbed the rope, and Aunt Sue tied
cried
the other end to the sled. Then she said, "pull!"

The dogs barked and pulled hard. Beth

gripped the reins. The team pulled the man free
You're   exclaimed
just as the ice split open. "Your safe now," Beth said.
gasped   ⌗
"Thank you!" the man said. "You saved my life!"

Then follow these strategies to proofread your draft:

- **Reread your revised paper several times.** Check for different types of errors each time.

- **Check for punctuation errors.** Be sure you used commas and end punctuation correctly.

- **Check each sentence for correct capitalization.** Be sure to use capitals to begin each sentence and with state names, city names, and people's names.

- **Check for correct grammar and usage.** Be sure you have used complete sentences.

- **Check for spelling mistakes.** Read your paper from the bottom to the top, word for word, to spot errors more easily.

TECHNOLOGY TIP!

A spell-checker will not point out words that have been left out of a sentence. It's important to use the spell-checker and read over your work yourself. Read carefully to be sure you do not "see" words that are not there!

CHECKLIST: PROOFREADING

- [ ] Did you spell all the words correctly?
- [ ] Did you use commas and end punctuation correctly?
- [ ] Did you use capital letters where needed?
- [ ] Did you avoid errors in grammar and usage?

Publish and Present

After revising and editing, you may choose to publish your writing to share with others.

The writer used the Before You Publish checklist while reviewing her story one last time. Read "Team to the Rescue!" and talk with a partner about the story. Do you think that the story was ready to be published? Why or why not?

Team to the Rescue!

One cold winter afternoon, Beth and her Aunt Sue were mushing across a frozen lake in Alaska. There wasn't much daylight left, and Beth wanted to get back to camp before dark. She and Sue were tired.

All of a sudden, Beth saw something moving on the ice. "Look, Aunt Sue!" she shouted, pointing ahead. When they got closer, they saw a man clinging to the edge of a hole in the ice.

Aunt Sue slid a thick rope across the ice. The man grabbed the rope, and Aunt Sue tied the other end to the sled. Then she cried, "Pull!"

The dogs barked and pulled hard. Beth gripped the reins. The team pulled the man free just as the ice split open. "You're safe now," Beth exclaimed.

"Thank you!" the man gasped. "You saved my life!"

—Jessica Peters

Practice

- Check your revised story one more time.

- Make a neat, final copy. Use a computer if it is available

- Add illustrations or an appropriate background drawing. If you are using a computer, add clip art or other images.

After you publish, share your story with others. You may wish to post it on a class Web site or read it aloud. Use this rubric to help evaluate your published piece.

Writing Rubric: Story

Score	Description
4 **Excellent**	<ul><li>creates an entertaining detailed story</li><li>moves readers through an engaging beginning, middle, and end</li><li>uses original voice and well-crafted dialogue</li><li>uses concrete details and sensory language</li><li>uses a variety of transitions</li><li>is free or almost free of errors</li></ul>
3 **Good**	<ul><li>creates a solid, detailed story</li><li>creates a clear beginning, middle, and end</li><li>attempts to create a personal style</li><li>uses some concrete details and sensory language</li><li>uses some transitions</li><li>has minor errors that do not confuse the reader</li></ul>
2 **Fair**	<ul><li>attempts to create a story with some details</li><li>has an unclear beginning, middle and end</li><li>lacks involvement with readers</li><li>uses words that are unclear with no figurative language</li><li>uses few transitions</li><li>makes frequent errors that confuse the reader</li></ul>
1 **Unsatisfactory**	<ul><li>does not tell a story</li><li>has no beginning, middle, or end</li><li>shows no engagement with the readers</li><li>uses words not connected to the purpose</li><li>does not use transitions</li><li>makes serious and repeated errors</li></ul>

TECHNOLOGY TIP!

Use available technology to share your writing.

- E-mail your published piece to your teacher or classmates.
- Display your writing on an electronic white board.
- Record it and save it as an audio file so others can listen to it on an mp3 player.

CHECKLIST: BEFORE YOU PUBLISH

☐ Did I consider the purpose for my story?

☐ Did I think about my audience as I wrote? Will my audience find the story entertaining?

☐ Did I give details about the characters in my story?

☐ Did I create a plot with a clear beginning, middle, and end?

☐ Did I include and describe an interesting setting?

☐ Did I use dialogue words to vary the characters' responses?

☐ Did I include dialogue and write it correctly?

☐ Did I make sure my sentences flowed smoothly? Did I combine sentences when necessary?

☐ Did I proofread and correct all my errors?

Lesson A
The Writing Process

Writers use a five-step writing process to develop their writing. Whether you are writing a narrative story, an informative/explanatory essay, or an opinion piece, you can use the writing process to turn your ideas into a polished final draft.

1 Prewrite
- Decide why you are writing and who will read it.
- Choose a topic.
- Gather ideas.
- Organize your ideas.

2 Draft
- Use your notes from prewriting.
- Get your ideas down on paper.
- Don't worry about mistakes.

3 Revise
- Add details and ideas.
- Delete ideas that are off topic.
- Substitute more interesting words.
- Rearrange sentences or parts of sentences.

4 Edit
- Check your spelling.
- Fix punctuation mistakes.
- Fix capitalization mistakes.
- Fix other grammar mistakes.

5 Publish
- Choose a format.
- Neatly print or type a final draft.
- Add visuals.

6 Present
- Share with your audience.

These are the five steps of the writing process.

- Prewrite
- Draft
- Revise
- Edit
- Publish/Present

Prewrite

The purpose of prewriting is to create a plan before you begin to write. During prewriting, writers think about and gather the ideas that they will need.

Study the Model and Practice

As you're prewriting, it's important to consider the following.

Purpose and Audience

Writers have many different purposes for writing. They may write to entertain, inform, or convince readers to share a point of view. Writers may also write for many different audiences. Writers think about their audience by deciding who will read their writing.

Look at this student model. Who is the audience? What is the purpose?

> Visit Santa Fe and you'll know why it is called the City Different. It is unlike any city I have ever visited. The first thing you notice are the beautiful old buildings that line the narrow, winding streets. The Plaza is the heart of the old town. Here you see buildings from the 1600s, Native Americans selling handmade jewelry, and shops displaying Santa Fe specialties.

Before you start writing, think about why you are writing. Think about who your audience will be.

THINK AND WRITE

Audience How does thinking about your audience help you decide what tone of voice you should use in your writing? Will your writing be more serious because of the subject and audience? Or will your writing be more casual to match an audience of people you know?

Common Core State Standards Literacy Handbook

Choose a Topic

Begin by **brainstorming** a list of topics. Start with things you are interested in or topics that you want to learn more about. Use the list to choose a topic that interests you and will interest other people, too.

After choosing a topic, **gather ideas** and information that you want to include in your writing. Jot your ideas down on a piece of paper.

Santa Fe, New Mexico

Went there last year
Ate a lot of good food
Saw interesting buildings
Saw Native American art
Walked around a lot
Weather was nice

Organize Your Ideas

The next step in prewriting is organizing your ideas. Remember your purpose and audience. Then decide the best way to share your ideas with your readers. If you are telling a story, for example, you will want to put the main events in sequence, or the order in which they happen. If you are writing a report, you may wish to group your ideas according to the key points you plan to make.

Writers often use a graphic organizer to help organize their ideas.

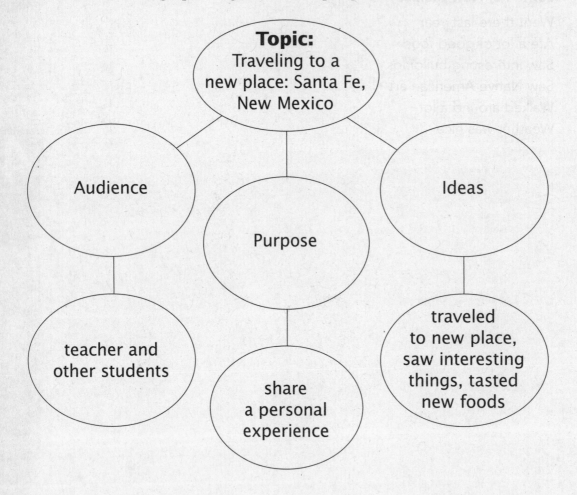

Research

Once you have organized your ideas, look them over and decide whether or not you need to gather more details and information. You may need to do some research before you begin writing.

For example, if you are writing a story, you may wish to use a thesaurus to find clear, precise words that describe your characters and setting. If you are writing a report, you may need to use additional resources to find facts, details, quotations, or examples that support and explain your topic.

This writer used travel brochures from her trip to remind her of specific details about Santa Fe.

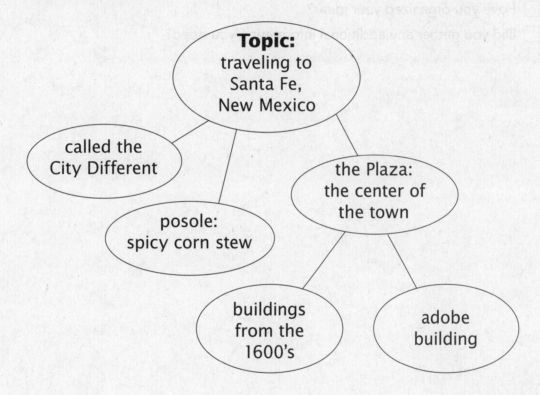

TECHNOLOGY TIP!
An online dictionary, thesaurus, or encyclopedia is a great place to find interesting words or facts to add to your writing.

CHECKLIST: PREWRITING
- [ ] Have you thought about your purpose and audience?
- [ ] Have you brainstormed topic ideas?
- [ ] Have you chosen your topic and listed what you know about it?
- [ ] Have you organized your ideas?
- [ ] Did you gather any additional information you need?

Draft

Now that you have gathered your ideas, you are ready to begin drafting. When you write a first draft, you get your ideas down on paper. Write as much as you can about your topic. Don't worry about making mistakes. You can fix them later when you revise and edit.

Practice

As you draft,

- use the graphic organizer you created during prewriting.
- think about a way to grab your reader's attention at the beginning of your writing.
- organize your details in a way that makes sense.
- give your readers a sense of closure at the end.

> **TECHNOLOGY TIP!**
> Are you typing your draft? Follow these tips.

Keyboarding Skills

When you type on a keyboard, rest the fingers of your left hand on the **A**, **S**, **D**, and **F** keys. Rest the fingers of your right hand on the **J**, **K**, **L**, and **;** keys. Place your thumbs on the space bar. These keys are called the *home keys*. When you rest your fingers on these keys, it is easy to reach other characters on the keyboard.

Stockbyte

Practice

Look at the keyboard on page 377. Then answer the questions.

- Which finger would you use to type a lowercase **g**?
  You would use your left index finger.
- Which finger would you use to type a lowercase **w**?
  You would use your left ring finger.
- Which fingers would you use to type an uppercase **N**?
  You would use your left pinky finger on the shift key and right index
  finger on the N key.

Now practice typing these sentences. Use the home keys as the resting
place for your fingers. When you finish, check for errors. Time yourself,
and see if you can type it again in a shorter amount of time. Continue to
practice typing and retyping this passage until you can type one full page
in a single sitting.

> Can you make a rainbow with a garden hose? If you've
> stood with your back to the sun and looked at the fine mist
> from a hose, fountain, or waterfall, you've probably seen a
> rainbow form.
>
> You can also make a rainbow indoors. Fill a clear plastic cup
> about halfway with water. Carefully place it on the edge of a
> table. A third of it should extend over the edge. Hold a piece
> of white paper directly behind the cup. Shine a flashlight
> vertically through the bottom of the cup. You should see a
> rainbow on the paper.

CHECKLIST: DRAFTING

- ☐ Does your writing fit your purpose and audience?
- ☐ Did you stick to your topic?
- ☐ Have you included interesting facts or specific details to develop the topic?
- ☐ Did you organize your writing in a logical way?

Revise

Once you have completed your draft, the next step is to revise it. Revising is a chance to make sure your ideas are clear and coherent, or understandable. Writers revise their writing before it is published to make sure their readers can understand the message.

Study the Model and Practice

Look at how the student writer revises her draft about a trip to Santa Fe.

> Visit Santa Fe and you'll know why it is called The City Different.
> ~~Santa Fe is also known as The City Different.~~ It is
>
> unlike any city I have ever visited. The first think you
>
> notice are the ^beautiful old^ adobe buidings that line the ^narrow, winding^ streets.
>
> The Plaza is the ^heart^ ~~center~~ of the old town. Here you
>
> see buildings from the 1600's Native Americans
>
> selling their ^handmade^ jewelry, and shops displaying Santa
>
> Fe specialties. ~~But shopping id expensive.~~ If you're
>
> hungry, you need to try the posole. ^a spicy corn stew^ As beautiful as
>
> the city is, the surrounding mountains, sunsets, and ^the amazing^
>
> ^the dazzling^ stars at night take your breath away. One visit is
>
> never enough to The City Different.

Then revise your own draft. When you revise, reread your draft to

- add details and ideas to make the message clearer and more interesting,
- delete unnecessary details and ideas that are not related to your topic,
- substitute more interesting words for dull or repetitive language, and
- rearrange sentences and sentence parts to make them clearer.

Peer Conferencing

During the revision stage, writers often share their draft with a peer to get more feedback. It is helpful to have a partner review your draft and make suggestions for improvements. Having another person read your writing can help you determine if your message is clear and coherent, or understandable.

Follow these steps to conduct a peer conference:

- Exchange drafts with a partner.
- Read the draft.
- Tell what you liked about it.
- Ask questions to make sure you understood your partner's ideas.
- Make suggestions for improvement.

Use your partner's comments and suggestions to help you decide what changes need to be made when you revise.

TECHNOLOGY TIP!

If you used a word processor to type your draft, you can e-mail the draft to your peer or your teacher for feedback. Ask your partner or teacher to add comments in a different color font so you can easily find them.

CHECKLIST: REVISING

- ☐ Does your writing fit your purpose and audience?
- ☐ Do you need to elaborate on any ideas you have included?
- ☐ Did you present ideas or events in a logical order?
- ☐ Did you use transition words to link one idea to the next?
- ☐ Do your sentences flow together?

Edit

After you have revised your draft, you will need to proofread it to correct errors in grammar, mechanics and usage, and spelling. Use these proofreading marks to mark errors on your draft.

PROOFREADING MARKS

⌗ new paragraph

∧ add

♪ take out

≡ Make a capital letter.

/ Make a small letter.

ⓢⓟ Check the spelling.

⊙ Add a period.

Study the Model and Practice

Look at the proofreading corrections made on the draft shown below. What does the ≡ symbol mean? When does the writer use that symbol?

Santa Fe is also known as The City Different. It is unlike any city I have ever visited. The first think you notice are the adobe buidings that line the streets. The Plaza is the center of the old town. Here you ~~saw~~ *see* buildings from the 1600's native americans selling their ~~jewlry~~ *jewelry*, and shops displaying Santa Fe specialties. But shopping id expensive. If ~~your~~ *you're* hungry, you need to try the posole. As ~~beautyful~~ *beautiful* as the city is, the surrounding mountains, sunsets, and stars at night ~~took~~ *take* your breath away. One visit is never enough to The City Different⊙

Then follow these strategies to proofread your own draft:

- **Reread your revised paper several times.** Check for different types of errors each time.

- **Check for punctuation errors.** Be sure you used commas and end punctuation correctly.

- **Check each sentence for correct capitalization.** Be sure to use capitals to begin sentences and for street names, city names, and people's names.

- **Check for correct grammar and usage.** Be sure you don't have any fragments or run-on sentences.

- **Check for spelling mistakes.** Read your paper from the bottom to the top, word for word, to spot errors more easily.

TECHNOLOGY TIP!
Spell-checkers don't find homophones, words that sound the same but have different spellings. Be sure to check carefully for the correct use of words such as *to, too,* and *two.*

CHECKLIST: PROOFREADING
☐ Did you spell all the words correctly?
☐ Did you use commas and end punctuation correctly?
☐ Did you use capital letters where needed?
☐ Did you fix any errors in grammar or usage?

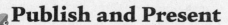

Publish and Present

After revising and editing, you may choose to publish your writing to share with others. When writers publish their writing, they produce a clean, neat final draft that is free of errors.

When you publish your writing, be sure to include a title and your name. If you have access to a computer, type your final draft so it is easy to read.

Practice

- Give your revised draft one more careful look.
- Make a neat final copy.
- If you wish, add maps, charts, photographs, or illustrations to your writing.

After you publish, share your writing with others. You may wish to post it on a class Web site or read it aloud.

TECHNOLOGY TIP!

Use technology to publish your writing:
- Type your draft on a word processor. Use a font that is easy to read.
- Save your work often.
- Learn how to use your computer to insert charts, graphs, or clip art in your writing.

Share your final draft:
- e-mail it to your teacher and classmates.
- post it on your class or school Web site.
- submit it to an online literary magazine, or displaying it on an electronic whiteboard.

CHECKLIST: BEFORE YOU PUBLISH

- [ ] Who was my audience? Will my writing be clear to them?
- [ ] What was my purpose for writing? Did I organize my information so that my audience can understand it?
- [ ] Did I add a title?
- [ ] Did I include details and facts that support my topic?
- [ ] Did I present my ideas in a logical order?
- [ ] Did I organize my paragraphs so that the ideas flow smoothly?
- [ ] Did I check for mistakes in grammar?
- [ ] Did I correct all errors in capitalization and punctuation?

Lesson A
Use the Research Process

Writers often use a research process to investigate a topic and answer a question. In this lesson, you will choose a topic and formulate a question about your topic. Then you will gather information to answer your question.

Develop a Research Plan

Before you begin researching, you must develop a plan. What will you research? Where will you find information?

Study the Model and Practice

Choosing a topic is the first step in developing your research plan.

Choose a Topic

To begin the research process, choose a topic that interests you. You might consider researching a historical event, such as the Civil Rights movement. Or you may be interested to find out more about an area of scientific study, such as space travel or endangered species.

To get ideas for topics you might like to research, look back at some informational texts you have read recently. Jot your ideas down on a sheet of paper. Discuss your ideas with a partner, and share why you find these topics interesting. Then choose the topic that you would like to research.

This student recently saw a documentary movie about Africa and wanted to find out more. Here are some topics she considered.

> **Topic Ideas**
> • Endangered species
> • Plants that grow in Africa
> • What it's like to live in Africa
> • Elephants in Africa

Develop a Question

Write a list of questions you have about your topic. You will choose one of these questions to investigate throughout the rest of the research process.

A good research question is **open ended**. For example, the question *What are some different kinds of cultural dances?* can be answered just by making a list. However, *Why do some cultures make up dances?* can be researched in depth and answered in many ways.

A good research question is also **manageable**. For example, the question *What are the different kinds of plants in the world?* is very broad. It would be very difficult to answer this question well because there is too much to say about it. Instead, you might ask *Why are there so few plants in deserts?* This question is narrower. It would be possible to research and answer this question well.

Read this question.

> Which animals are endangered?

Now read this revision.

> Why are African elephants endangered?

Think about why this revision is a better research question.

Review your list of questions. Discuss them with a partner, and choose a question to research.

Identify Sources

Once you have developed your research question, think about where you will find information about your topic. Brainstorm a list of sources you might use.

Be sure to use a variety of sources to conduct your research. It is important to use several different sources to research your topic, so you can be sure the information you find is correct. Different sources can also give you different types of information. This will provide you with a broader picture of your topic.

Use your school's media center, the public library, and the Internet to gather your resources.

Here is a list of different types of sources you might consider for your research.

Print	Internet	Film and Radio	Experiences
Almanacs	Digital books	Educational television shows	Live interviews
Atlases	Informational Web sites	Radio broadcasts	Making observations
Autobiographies	Online news articles	Documentary movies	Attending live events
Encyclopedias	Online encyclopedias		Recalling personal experiences
Informational books	Podcasts		
Magazines			
Maps			
Newspapers			

TECHNOLOGY TIP!

When using a search engine to find online resources, use the Advanced Search function and limit your search results to Web sites that end in *.gov* or *.edu*. These types of Web sites provide reliable information.

Evaluate Sources

Evaluate sources to decide whether or not you should use them for your research. Use this checklist to help you.

CHECKLIST: CRITERIA FOR EVALUATION SOURCES

Relevant

☐ The information closely matches my topic and research question.

Authoritative

☐ The author is an expert in this subject.

☐ The author includes a bibliography.

☐ The Internet address ends in .edu or .gov.

Current

☐ The date on which the information was printed or posted is shown. It is within one or two years of today's date. (If the source provides information about past events, the date is not so important.)

Objective

☐ The purpose of the source is to inform (not to persuade or to entertain).

☐ The information is based on facts.

☐ The author gives proof to support his or her ideas.

Accurate

☐ I found other sources that provide the same or similar information.

Collect Information

Once you have gathered a variety of sources, you will take notes to find information that answers your research question.

Study the Model and Practice

Next, you will take notes to find information that answers your research questions.

Take Notes

Taking notes means writing down information from the sources you gathered for research. Good notes contain key phrases and short sentences that sum up important facts and ideas.

When you take notes, follow these guidelines:

- Record the title, author, and publication date for each source you use.
- Create subject headings and use them to organize your notes.
- Include only the most important information about the topic.
- Write notes in your own words.
- Keep your notes short.

Characteristics of African elephants:
All about Elephants by Georgia E. Ellis, 2010
- largest land mammal
- big ears keep them cool

"Saving the African Elephant," New York Times, March 3, 2009
- tusks made of ivory

Why they are endangered:
"Saving the African Elephant," New York Times, March 3, 2009
- illegal to trade elephant ivory, but poachers do it anyway

"African Elephants," Smithsonian National Zoological Park Web site, 2010
- poachers cut population nearly in half
- also lost habitat to ranches and farms

Organize and Synthesize Information

Now that you have gathered facts and details about your topic, you will organize your ideas and think about how they answer your research question.

Study the Model and Practice

Organize

Organize your information by sorting the facts and details you gathered into categories. Use a graphic organizer such as a three- or four-column chart, a concept web, or a time line to help you organize your information.

Research Question: Why are African elephants endangered?		
Characteristics	**Causes**	**Effects**
–largest land mammal –live in savanna or in forests –use tusks for protection, to dig, or move things out of the way –don't like to be around people –travel a lot to find food	–poachers kill elephants for their tusks –ranches and farms have taken over habitats	–population has been cut in half –now found mostly in reserves, not in the wild

Synthesize

Now that you have organized your information, stop and think about how your research helps you answer the research question you developed. Look for connections among the facts and details you found. Finding these connections can lead to new understandings about your topic.

To synthesize your findings

- group similar ideas together
- draw a conclusion about what these ideas have in common
- write a sentence that summarizes each of these new understandings

This writer underlined similar information and wrote a synthesis based on these similar parts.

Research Question: Why are African elephants endangered?		
Characteristics	**Causes**	**Effects**
-largest land mammal -live in savanna or in forests -use tusks for protection, to dig, or move things out of the way -don't like to be around people -travel a lot to find food	-poachers kill elephants for their tusks -ranches and farms have taken over habitats	-population has been cut in half -now found mostly in reserves, not in the wild

Synthesis: I can draw the conclusion that the African elephant's tusks are both necessary and endangering. They are tools they use to stay alive, but they are also the main cause for their endangered status.

Develop a Presentation

Develop a presentation to share your research findings with others. You may wish to write a report, give a speech, or build a Web page to present your ideas. What are some other ways you could present your findings?

Whatever format you choose, be sure to share your research question and what you learned from your investigation. Think of two or three key points you would like to share, and provide some facts, details, or examples that explain each point.

Gather any charts, photographs, illustrations, maps, or other visual aids you wish to include.

Be sure to include a list of the sources you used to gather your information. Cite the title, author, publisher, and publication date for each source.

Practice

Follow these steps to develop your presentation.

1. Decide on a format to present your findings.
2. Choose two or three key points, or main ideas, you would like to share.
3. Add facts, details, or examples that explain each point.
4. Create or print out any visual aids you would like to include.
5. Create a list of the sources you used.

Go to Lesson 5.2 Lesson A **Present a Report** on Volume 2 page 25 to learn more about delivering a presentation.

Lesson B
Use Text Evidence

Writers often use text evidence from literary and informational text to analyze, reflect, or research.

- Writers use text evidence as they **analyze** text to better understand it.
- Writers use text evidence as they **reflect** on text to develop a personal response to it.
- Writers use text evidence to **research** a topic to answer a question.

Text evidence supports their analysis, reflection, or research. Text evidence includes facts, details, or quotations that support or explain a writer's topic.

Analyze Literary Text

Writers analyze stories to better understand what they read. Writers may analyze story elements such as characters, plot, or setting. They may analyze literary elements and devices such as theme, point of view, or figurative language.

Learning from Writers

Read the example of literary analysis.

Literary Analysis: Student Model

"Zlateh the Goat" is a short story by Isaac Bashevis Singer. The title explains that Zlateh is a goat. By the time I finished reading, though, I thought Zlateh was more like a person.

Zlateh can't talk, but the boy, Aaron, imagines that she is saying different things. At the beginning, Aaron is supposed to sell Zlateh. He imagines that she asks him where they are going. Pretty soon they get stuck in a bad snow storm. Aaron and Zlateh have an imaginary conversation. All Zlateh really says is, "Maaaa," but the narrator says that "it meant many things" to Aaron.

The author also makes Zlateh seem human because she takes care of Aaron during the storm. Aaron drinks her milk. He stays warm by cuddling with her. She listens to his stories. The narrator even says that Zlateh was "like a sister." She feeds him and comforts him.

The author does a good job of making Zlateh seem like a human being. I was happy that Aaron didn't have to sell her at the end. She was part of the family.

Choose a Topic

To analyze a story, writers first decide what it is they would like to think more about. After reading, stop to consider what stood out in the story. For example, perhaps the author used interesting figurative language. You may decide to analyze the use of figurative language in the story.

In this model, the writer describes the story's main character, Zlateh. The topic sentence is underlined below.

"Zlateh the Goat" is a short story by Isaac Bashevis Singer. The title explains that Zlateh is a goat. <u>By the time I finished reading, though, I thought Zlateh was more like a person.</u>

Practice

Choose a topic for your own analytical essay.

1. Read the prompt below. You will write an analytical response to a story you have read recently.

2. To get started, choose a familiar story that has an interesting character, setting, or event. What stood out to you? Write your ideas on a sheet of paper.

3. Choose an idea you would like to write about.

> Describe in depth a character, setting, or event in a story. Draw on specific details in the text, such as a character's thoughts, words, or actions.

Find Evidence

To find evidence, skim and scan for chapter titles, images, or key words that support your topic. For example, this writer uses details and quotations from the story to show how Zlateh seems like a human. When the writer looked back through the story, she used the key word *Zlateh* and looked for quotation marks to find words that Zlateh "spoke."

Page Number	Text Evidence
Page 3	Zlateh seems to ask a question about where they are going.
Page 4	Aaron drinks Zlateh's milk. He cuddles with her for warmth. They talk together.
Page 5	"Maaaa" means many things to Aaron. Zlateh is "like a sister."

Practice

Find evidence for your own analytical essay.

1. Make a list of key words that will help you locate information that relates to your topic.

2. Look back through the story. Skim and scan to find details and quotations.

3. Use a two-column chart to record the page number and evidence you find.

Organize Ideas

Next, organize the text evidence to support your topic. This writer groups evidence into categories: *Zlateh Says* and *Zlateh Does*.

Zlateh Says	Zlateh Does
seems to ask a question about where they are going	Aaron drinks Zlateh's milk.
"talks" to Aaron	Aaron cuddles with her for warmth.
says only, "Maaaa," but it means many different things to Aaron	Zlateh acts "like a sister."

Practice

Organize evidence for your own analytical essay. Use a graphic organizer to organize your text evidence. You may wish to use a sequence chart to list evidence in order of importance or in time order. Or you may wish to use a Venn diagram to compare and contrast.

Write

Now that you have gathered and organized your text evidence, you are ready to begin writing. To write an analytical essay about the story you chose, begin by telling readers your topic. Then use text evidence to write sentences that support and explain your topic. Be sure to end your paragraph by giving readers a sense of closure.

In this paragraph, the writer begins with a main idea and then supports it with details and quotations. The details and quotations are underlined.

> Zlateh can't talk, but the boy, Aaron, imagines that she is saying different things. At the beginning, Aaron is supposed to sell Zlateh. He imagines that she asks him where they are going. Pretty soon they get stuck in a bad snow storm. Aaron and Zlateh have an imaginary conversation. All Zlateh really says is, "Maaaa," but the narrator says that "it meant many things" to Aaron.

Common Core State Standards Literacy Handbook

Practice

Write your own analytical essay.

1. Use your graphic organizer to write an essay about the story you have chosen.

2. Be sure to use quotation marks around words a character said.

3. At the end, restate your topic sentence or leave your readers with something to think about.

Reflect on Text

Writers reflect on a text they have read in order to think more deeply about it. When you reflect on reading, you evaluate, or make judgments, about how well the author achieved his or her purpose. To write a reflection, writers

- determine the author's main idea,

- evaluate the reasons and evidence the author uses to support the main idea, and

- respond to the text by sharing personal connections and feelings.

4

Learning from Writers

Read a student's reflection on an informational text.

Text Analysis: Student Model

The Superman of Jay Blanchard Park

Superman isn't just a character in comic books, games, and movies. There's a real live Superman at work in Florida's Jay Blanchard Park. At least that's what Sy Montgomery says in her essay "The Eco-Canoeist." Based on what she has to say, the person called the "Eco-Canoeist" really is just like Superman.

The river in Jay Blanchard Park is full of trash. This place needs a hero. That hero is Steve Nordlinger, the Eco-Canoeist, who cleans up the river in his spare time. The author says, "Steve seems like a superhero straight out of a comic book." In the conclusion, she calls him "part Superman."

Nordlinger reminds the author of Superman because he is very strong. Nordlinger doesn't just pull cans and plastic bottles from the river. He pulls out truck tires, refrigerators, car parts, doghouses, and even sofas! I can't imagine pulling a sofa out of a river, much less one that is drenched in dirty river water. By doing these amazing physical feats, Nordlinger definitely deserves to be called Superman.

Nordlinger puts what he believes into action, just like Superman. Like Superman, when there's trouble, he rushes in. Also like Superman, he doesn't do it for fame or money. In fact, at first, no one even knew who was cleaning up the river. That is pretty admirable, if you ask me.

I think Montgomery's comparison of Steve Nordlinger to Superman makes sense. Only someone as powerful and good as Superman could "rescue" the river in Jay Blanchard Park.

Determine the Main Idea

To write a reflection, writers first choose a text that stood out to them. The topic of the text may be one that is personally interesting or important to the writer. A writer may also choose a text in which the author made a point particularly well—or particularly poorly.

Once you choose a text you would like to reflect on, determine the author's main idea. Ask yourself, "What is this selection mostly about? What is the author trying to explain?"

In this model, the writer begins by restating the author's main idea. Why do you think the writer chose to write about this text?

> Superman isn't just a character in comic books, games, and movies. There's a real live Superman at work in Florida's Jay Blanchard Park. At least that's what Sy Montgomery says in her essay "The Eco-Canoeist." Based on what she has to say, the person called the "Eco-Canoeist" really is just like Superman.

Practice

Choose a text for your own personal reflection.

1. Read the prompt below. You will write a personal reflection on an informational text you have read recently.

2. To get started, choose an informational text that you remember well. Did you enjoy it? Why or why not? Did the author do a good job explaining the topic? Write your ideas on a sheet of paper.

3. Choose a text you would like to write about.

Identify and Evaluate Evidence

Did the author use facts, details, examples, or quotations to support the main idea? Skim and scan the text to identify the reasons and evidence the author used. Then decide whether or not you think these reasons and evidence do a good job supporting the main idea.

Evaluating Evidence

Good evidence includes...
- facts that are used accurately to support the main idea.
- details and examples that are closely related to the main idea.
- quotations from experts on the topic.

Faulty evidence includes...
- unsupported opinions.
- details or examples that aren't relevant.
- quotations from people who aren't experts on the topic.

For example, this writer used a chart to record the author's evidence and evaluate how well it supports the main idea.

Main Idea of the Text: Steve Nordlinger is just like Superman.

Text Evidence	Does this support the main idea? Why or why not?
The river is polluted and needs a hero.	Yes. It shows that the Eco-Canoeist's work is heroic, like Superman.
"Steve seems like a superhero straight out of a comic book."	Yes. It shows that the Eco-Canoeist is like a superhero.
He pulls out truck tires, refrigerators, car parts, doghouses, and even sofas!	Yes. This shows that he is really strong, like Superman.
No one knew who was cleaning it up for a while. He doesn't want credit.	No one knew Clark Kent was Superman.

Practice

Identify and evaluate evidence for your own personal reflection.

1. Write the main idea at the top of a two-column chart. Then skim and scan the selection to find the evidence the author uses to support or explain the main idea. Look for facts, details, examples, or quotations. Write the evidence in the left column.

2. Look over the evidence you have recorded. Decide whether or not it supports or explains the author's main idea.

3. Use a two-column chart to record the page number and evidence you find.

Develop a Personal Response

Writers include a personal response to the text they are writing about. They think about personal connections they made to the text. They share their personal reactions to the author's ideas.

Make Connections

Did an example or detail from the text remind you of something? Making connections to your own experiences, to the world around you, or to other reading will help you better understand a text.

React to the Reading

Did a particular fact or detail stand out to you? Why? Noticing the way a text makes you think or feel will also help you better understand it.

Main Idea of the Text: Steve Nordlinger is just like Superman.

Text Evidence	Does this support the main idea? Why or why not?	Personal Response
The river is polluted and needs a hero.	Yes. It shows that the Eco-Canoeist's work is heroic, like Superman.	
"Steve seems like a superhero straight out of a comic book."	Yes. It shows that the Eco-Canoeist is like a superhero.	
He pulls out truck tires, refrigerators, car parts, doghouses, and even sofas!	Yes. This shows that he is really strong, like Superman.	I can't imagine being strong enough to pull a wet sofa out of a dirty river!
No one knew who was cleaning it up for a while. He doesn't want credit.	No one knew Clark Kent was Superman.	It's pretty admirable that he didn't want any credit.

Practice

Develop a personal response for your own reflection.

1. Think back to when you read the text for the first time. Which part was your favorite? What did you like about it? Jot down your ideas.

2. Look over the text evidence you recorded. Do any of the facts, details, examples, or quotations remind you of your own experiences? Add a third column to your graphic organizer and record your personal connections or reactions.

Organize Ideas

Next, organize your ideas in a logical order. For example, you may wish to present the author's evidence from strongest to weakest. You may wish to add your personal connections as you go along, or you may use a paragraph at the end to share your personal response.

This writer used a sequence chart to organize his ideas according to Superman's traits.

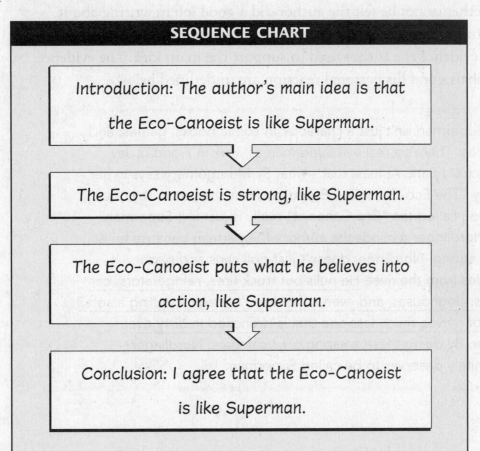

SEQUENCE CHART

Introduction: The author's main idea is that the Eco-Canoeist is like Superman.

The Eco-Canoeist is strong, like Superman.

The Eco-Canoeist puts what he believes into action, like Superman.

Conclusion: I agree that the Eco-Canoeist is like Superman.

Practice

Organize ideas for your own personal reflection.

1. Look at the text evidence you recorded. Which evidence is the strongest? Which evidence do you connect with personally? You may wish to use this evidence at the beginning of your reflection.

2. Decide how you will include the rest of the evidence you have gathered.

Write

Now that you have organized your text evidence and personal response, you are ready to begin writing. Begin your reflection by restating the author's main idea. Then explain how well the author uses evidence to support or explain this main idea. Be sure to include your own personal response to the text. Did you like it? Did you agree with the author? Why or why not?

In the first paragraph, the writer restates the author's main idea and tells readers whether or not he felt the author did a good job in writing about this topic. In the next paragraph, he explains his response by sharing and explaining evidence the author used to support the main idea. The evidence the writer shares and his personal reaction are underlined below.

> Superman isn't just a character in comic books, games, and movies. There's a real live Superman at work in Florida's Jay Blanchard Park. At least that's what Sy Montgomery says in her essay "The Eco-Canoeist." Based on what she has to say, the person called the "Eco-Canoeist" really is just like Superman.
>
> Nordlinger reminds the author of Superman because he is very strong. Nordlinger doesn't just pull cans and plastic bottles from the river. He pulls out truck tires, refrigerators, car parts, doghouses, and even sofas! I can't imagine pulling a sofa out of a river, much less one that is drenched in dirty river water. By doing these amazing physical feats, Nordlinger definitely deserves to be called Superman.

Practice

Write your own personal reflection.

1. Use your graphic organizer to write a reflection about the informational text you have chosen.

2. Use quotation marks when you use the exact words the author wrote.

3. Be sure to share your personal response to the text.

Research

Writers draw evidence from text when they research a topic. Finding text evidence from difference sources helps writers support and explain their research topic.

Learning from Writers

Read a student model of a research report that uses text evidence to explain the topic.

Research Report: Student Model

Poison Dart Frogs: Friend and Foe

In the hot, humid tropical rain forests of Central and South America, poison dart frogs live exotic lives. With their bright colors and their powerful venom, these stunning endangered animals are both friend and foe to humans.

The smallest species of poison dart frogs is less than 1.5 centimeters. Although they are small animals, poison dart frogs are hard to miss. What the frogs lack in size, they make up for with bright, brilliant colors and patterns. Poison dart frogs can be blue, purple, green, red, yellow, or orange. One might think that this bright coloring would attract predators, but it actually warns them to stay away.

Poison dart frogs are among the most toxic animals on Earth. One species has enough venom to kill 10 grown humans! Scientists aren't sure where the poison comes from, but they think the frogs take in plant poisons from the ants, termites, and beetles they eat.

The poison is dangerous, but it can be helpful too. For hundreds of years, people who live in the rain forest have put the poison in the tips of blowgun darts for hunting. The poison could be used for medicines too. Scientists are learning that a venom that usually causes pain might actually be able to be used as a painkiller!

Some people may say that endangered poison dart frogs are not worth saving because they are dangerous. We need to remember, however, that they also can help us.

Choose a Topic

Writers choose a topic that will interest their audience. Before they begin researching, writers formulate a question they would like to answer about their topic. A good research question is open-ended. It doesn't have a simple "yes" or "no" answer. To come up with a good question, you might try to think of questions that start with *how* or *why*.

In this model, the writer chose to write about poison dart frogs. The writer's topic sentence is underlined. Can you figure out what the writer's research question might have been?

> In the hot, humid tropical rain forests of Central and South America, poison dart frogs live exotic lives. <u>With their bright colors and their powerful venom, these stunning endangered animals are both friend and foe to humans.</u>

Practice

Choose a topic to research.

1. Brainstorm a list of topics you might like to research.

2. Think about your audience. Which topic would be most interesting to them? Choose one to write about.

3. Generate questions you have about your topic. Remember that a good research question is open-ended. Choose a question to research.

Gather Evidence

To find the answer to your research question, gather different sources about your topic. To find evidence from these sources, skim and scan for important information that relates to your question.

- Search for words or phrases printed in capitals, italics, or bold.
- Search for key words in section headings.
- Read the article's introduction to decide whether it has information you need.
- Read the topic sentence of each paragraph to discover if the information applies to your topic.
- Read the captions of photos, charts, graphs, and illustrations.

Research Question: *Why are poison dart frogs dangerous?*

Source	Text Evidence
encyclopedia	smallest species is less than 1.5 centimeters.
	may be blue, purple, green, red, yellow, or orange
Frogs Around the World by Earl Hamilton	Poison may be used as medicine.
	Some species have venom that can kill 10 grown people.

Practice

Find evidence that answers your own research question.

1. Use the media center or the Internet to gather resources related to your topic.

2. Make a list of key words that will help you locate information.

3. Skim and scan your sources to find facts, details, examples, or quotations that relate to your question.

4. Use a two-column chart to record the name of the source and the evidence you find.

Organize Ideas

Next, look over your text evidence. Do you have enough facts, details, examples, and quotations to answer your research question? If not, continue researching. Once you have enough evidence, organize the information you have gathered.

This writer used a three-column chart to organize the evidence she gathered.

Characteristics	Helpful	Harmful
small; some are less than 1.5 centimeters	may be able to use poison for medicine	Poison is really dangerous; one species has poison that can kill 10 grown people.
colorful: blue, purple, green, red, yellow, or orange	can use poison on the tips of arrows to hunt for food	
live in the rain forests in Central and South America		

Practice

Organize the evidence you have gathered to answer your own research question. Use a graphic organizer to organize your text evidence. You may wish to use a sequence chart to list evidence in order of importance or in time order. Or you may wish to use a Venn diagram to compare and contrast.

Write

Now that you have gathered and organized your text evidence, you are ready to begin writing. To write a response to a research question, begin by telling readers your topic. Then use text evidence to write sentences that support and explain your topic. Be sure to end your writing by giving readers a sense of closure.

In this paragraph, the writer begins with a topic sentence and then supports it with the facts, details, and examples she gathered while researching the topic. The facts and details are underlined below.

> The smallest species of poison dart frogs is less than 1.5 centimeters. Although they are small animals, poison dart frogs are hard to miss. What the frogs lack in size, they make up for with bright, brilliant colors and patterns. Poison dart frogs can be blue, purple, green, red, yellow, or orange. One might think that this bright coloring would attract predators, but it actually warns them to stay away.

Practice

Write a response to your own research question.

1. Begin by turning your research question into a topic sentence.

2. Use your text evidence graphic organizer as you write sentences that support and explain your topic sentence.

3. At the end, restate your topic sentence or leave your readers with something to think about.

Lesson A
Use a Writer's Notebook

Writers improve their skills by writing every day. There are many opportunities to write daily. Some involve informal writing such as e-mailing, sending text messages, writing notes, or posting on online message boards and social-networking sites. Others involve more serious writing, such as taking notes while reading, answering questions, and jotting down ideas and observations for future writing.

Set up a Writer's Notebook

Many writers use a notebook to record their writing. You can use a writer's notebook for many daily writing activities:

- Write a daily journal entry about your thoughts and reflections.
- Write personal responses to books you read.
- Start and add to a list of words you might like to use in your writing.
- Jot down ideas and observations you might want to use for future writing projects.

Writer's Notebook: Student Model

This writer used tabs to divide her notebook into different sections: Daily Journal, Response to Reading, Word Lists, Interesting Observations, and Writing Projects. Look at this example of a journal entry:

> September 25, 2010
>
> Last night I went to the grocery store with my mom. We ran into our neighbor, Mr. Berman, when we were there. I used to be afraid of him. He never smiles, and he always seems really unhappy. I thought he was mean. But last night, my mom talked to him, and I found out he isn't mean at all. He lives alone, and his only daughter goes to college far away. I think he's just lonely. I'm going to make sure I say hi to him when I see him from now on.

Practice and Apply

Follow these directions to start your own writer's notebook.

1. Start your own writer's notebook. Divide the notebook into sections using tabs, such as the ones shown on the previous page.

2. Write your name on the cover. You may wish to add pictures to personalize your notebook.

3. Write your first entry by responding to this writing prompt:

> *Write about your favorite thing to do outside of school.*

Daily Writing Prompts

Use your writer's notebook to practice writing daily. Use these prompts to spark your thinking.

Choose a prompt. Write your thoughts and ideas in your writer's notebook.

- Which person do you look up to? Why?
- What is one kind of technology you wouldn't want to live without? Why?
- Tell about your favorite place to go.
- How should schools deal with bullying?
- Which Web site do you visit regularly? What do you like about it?
- What hobby would you like to have? How could you get started?
- Would you like to be president some day? Why or why not?
- What's the best way to have fun?
- What's the best thing about where you live? What's the worst thing?
- What kind of pet would you recommend to someone?
- Should kids have to do chores? Why or why not?
- Should kids get allowances? Why or why not?
- Who is the most interesting person you know? Tell about them.
- What is your favorite book, and why?

- What do you think it would have been like to live a hundred years ago?
- What would it be like to travel to the moon?
- Why do you think teachers give homework? Does homework help you learn?
- What makes a good friend?
- What is one rule you wish your school enforced? Why?
- Who is a person you would like to get to know better? Why?

Writing Projects

You can also use a writer's notebook for longer writing activities:

- Record possible topics for longer writing projects such as
  - opinion pieces and book reviews on Volume 1 page 225
  - research reports and how-to pieces on Volume 1 page 269
  - personal narratives and stories on Volume 1 page 319
- Gather and organize ideas for writing projects.
- Record notes and sources from any research you gather.
- Draft, revise, and edit writing projects.

Practice writing longer projects by turning to the pages listed above. Use your writer's notebook as you prewrite and draft your piece of writing.